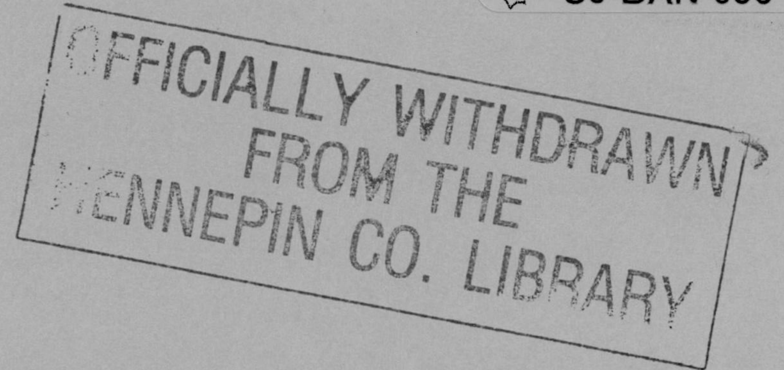

G·E·T HELP

SOLVING THE PROBLEMS ■ IN YOUR LIFE ■

G·E·T HELP

SOLVING THE PROBLEMS IN YOUR LIFE

SARA D. GILBERT

MORROW JUNIOR BOOKS/NEW YORK

Inquiries should be addressed to
William Morrow and Company, Inc.,
105 Madison Avenue,
New York, NY 10016.

Printed in the United States of America.
1 2 3 4 5 6 7 8 9 10

Library of Congress Cataloging-in-Publication Data
Gilbert, Sara D.
Get help: solving the problems in your life / by Sara D. Gilbert.
p. cm.
Bibliography: p.
Includes index.
Summary: Suggests how to recognize and admit the need for help
with various problems in life and how to locate help in such areas
as mental health, substance addiction, family problems, legal
matters, money, education, and physical health.
ISBN 0-688-08010-3.—ISBN 0-688-08928-3 (pbk.)
1. Mental health services—United States—Directories—Juvenile
literature. 2. Teenagers—Mental health services—United States—
Directories—Juvenile literature. [1. Mental health services—
Directories. 2. Life skills.] I. Title.
RA790.6.G53 1989
362.2′02573—dc19 88-32352 CIP AC

With thanks to those groups and individuals
that have been there
when *I* have needed to get help.

CONTENTS

ACKNOWLEDGMENTS

Get Help owes its existence to the information supplied by all of the organizations mentioned throughout its pages. The author wishes to thank them for their contributions to the book and to express her gratitude and congratulations for their ongoing, direct assistance to young people.

AUTHOR'S NOTE

Please keep in mind the following about the organizations included in *Get Help:*

- Their inclusion indicates that they exist as established resources for help and expertise—*and does not constitute an endorsement of their services.* Likewise, the omission of an existing service should not be interpreted as a negative judgment of its value.
- Although every effort has been made to be thorough, not all groups can be listed in a single book, especially as, over the life of a book, many organizations come and go, and phone numbers and addresses do not always remain constant. The cross-referencing and lists of general resources are intended to serve as backups for specific information that may have been omitted or that may change with time. *Readers are urged to contact resources listed in Chapter Four, "Backup," if they are unable to find solutions to their problems listed elsewhere within the book.*
- The selection of *any* resource requires personal judgment. The tips detailed in Chapter Three, "What to Ask," suggest techniques that should be used in checking out the qual-

ity and validity of service promised by any organization, whether listed in this book or not.

- The organizations listed in Chapter Two, "Where to Find Help," meet the same basic guidelines that anyone should follow in evaluating a helping service for young people:

They provide assistance or guidance for some of teenagers' most common problems.
They are able to help or inform young people directly and, except where noted, without parental involvement.
They are either very low in cost or *free of charge.*

The listings for this book were collected from directories, research and resource agencies, and social-service professionals and from information requested from the major national helping organizations.

Those entries marked with a ▲ are among the groups that responded to the author's request and that, by their own description of their services, are most likely to provide *direct* assistance to young people. Entries marked ■ are valuable, established sources for information about a problem and its solution or for referral to agencies that offer help.

WHY YOU NEED THIS BOOK

Youth is not "carefree" these days. Perhaps it never was, but today the difficulties that you face seem more hazardous than those of the past—and you are facing them with diminishing family and community support. But you *can* find help for your problems—if you know where to look.

That's why you need this book . . .

if you are bothered by worries that won't go away
if you counsel young people and seek professional help for them that is free and geared to meet their needs
if you wonder where in the world you can find solutions to some of today's most troubling situations.

CHAPTER ONE

HOW TO HELP YOURSELF

"I can do it *myself*!"
"But you don't understand . . ."
"I'm FINE!"
"*Nobody's* ever been in a mess like this!"

Do those phrases sound familiar? You hear them when someone is wrestling with a big personal problem. You've probably heard yourself say some of them.

How about: "I feel so *alone*!" We may not hear that one so often—but we probably say it, at least to ourselves. And we all have *felt* that way.

This book will show you that, no matter how you may feel, you are not, in fact, alone in facing even the most worrisome situation. It will show you that there are people out there who not only understand your situation but can help you—and *want* to help you—to find a solution. It's important that you believe that, or at least that you have a sense that it's true—because that is the first step in being able to *really* help yourself.

Here's another phrase—the simplest, but often the hardest to say: "I need help."

Those three words can take away the *alone* feeling and can, almost by themselves, solve whatever problem we have. You may know that and still have trouble with those words. Why are they so hard to say?

Well, let's take a look at some of the lessons most of us have learned since we were very young.

THE LESSONS WE'VE LEARNED

When you think about it, why should we believe we're not alone? Almost from the beginning of our lives, we're taught that it's good to do things for ourselves: "Look at little Johnny—he can climb the stairs all by himself! Isn't that wonderful?" parents coo.

We learn that we have to tie our shoes by ourselves . . . do our homework on our own . . . go away to camp and love it. You name it: independence is the big goal of growing up.

That's as it should be, because at some point we do have to cope with the real world on our own. But these days, many people must learn independence too young and too "well."

Today, most mothers work outside the home. Many families are held together by one parent instead of the traditional two. The older children often have responsibility not only for themselves but also for their younger siblings. More often than not, grandparents and other relatives are far away—and one-fourth of all American families relocate each year. So in addition to their extra responsibilities, young people lack the network of outside support they might once have relied on.

At the same time, they're asked to cope with some very "adult" problems their parents never had to face. Never before, for example, has adolescent adventure carried such a heavy price, now that drugs and AIDS deal death. Never before has education been so absolutely necessary—and so incredibly expensive.

The new stresses in the world create new problems for your parents, too—and you can feel that pressure. The very fact of having to handle all that you do may produce more problems to handle.

No wonder life sometimes seems overwhelming.

Add to all that another lesson many of us have learned from our families: "Don't wash your dirty linen in public." When there's trouble at home, we're taught to keep it at home.

Privacy is important, true. But when we keep our troubles sealed up in our homes or our heads, they fester and grow worse. Sometimes, all they need to dispel them is fresh air.

But we've been taught to be independent, right?

It's at this point that three new factors enter into the equations buzzing around our brains, factors that make asking for help even harder: *isolation*, *denial*, and *fear*.

WHY IT'S HARD TO ASK FOR HELP

When trouble comes, "independence" can quickly become *isolation*—a sense of being stranded on an island in a dangerous sea, a sea where everyone else seems to know how to swim.

"When my parents were splitting up, I felt awful," Robert says. "I knew they didn't want me to talk about it—they wouldn't talk about it to *me*. Lots of kids in my class had divorced parents, and they seemed to handle it fine, so I felt stupid, asking their advice."

Robert was finally forced to ask for help when his work and his behavior in school became so poor that he was at risk of being suspended. He was sent to someone who *wanted* to hear about his feelings, and he found a group of people who shared those feelings. Some of the other kids in his class, in fact. They were handling their problem "fine" because they had asked for help. Airing that "dirty linen" was all that Robert needed to do.

Sometimes, though, we don't even know that the linen is dirty. That's because of a factor in the self-defeating equation called *denial*. Families that just don't want to believe that one of their members has a drug problem, for instance, simply won't see the signs. Everyone else may know, and the family's ignorance may seem incredible, but their minds deny reality. In cases like that, denial can be deadly.

When Sandra got pregnant, she wouldn't admit it. It was hard *not* to know about her condition, and at some level, she did know—but it seemed so devastating that her mind simply made her believe that nothing was wrong. Denial again—denial that actually threatened her life before someone else noticed and got her medical attention.

Pregnancy, of course, is impossible to deny for long—but we often carry around less obvious worries without even admitting that we're troubled. It's important to get them out in the open, because they can be, literally, a drag: they keep us from getting the most out of life now, and they can even warp the future.

Because of the power of denial, which the mind uses as a protective device against pain, it's often necessary to look at the externals for a sense of what's going on inside.

Here are some of the events that commonly trigger trouble:

- A recent personal or family upheaval, ranging from a tornado or other natural disaster to something as "minor" as a change in schedule
- A legal or health-related crisis
- Divorce, remarriage, death, relocation, or job loss in the family
- Separation from a friend or an important adult
- Any significant transition, including switching schools or coming of age

Are any of those things going on in your life? Probably.

Even if our minds can't allow us to admit the existence of problems and the stress they secretly bring on, our bodies and behavior offer clues like these:

- Sleep troubles that are more than occasional
- Frequent headaches, stomachaches, or other

physical ailments for which there are no medical explanations
- Unexplainable difficulties with schoolwork or job
- Unease in dealing with other people
- Emotional overreactions to minor events
- A feeling of constant fatigue
- A need to move at top speed all the time
- Compulsion to overuse drugs of any sort, including caffeine or nicotine
- Constant hunger and weight gain, or lack of appetite and weight loss
- Involvement in an unusual number of petty problems or minor "accidents"

If you are experiencing two or more of these symptoms, it's time to take a look at what's troubling you. An easy way to do that is to read the topics listed in the contents and take note of the ones that strike a responsive chord.

It's okay not to be "fine"; everybody has troubles of some kind. The only mistake you can make is not dealing with them.

Perhaps you may not deny that you have a problem, but you're convinced that it can't be solved. That problem may be as scary and complex as addiction to a drug or as clear-cut and "simple" as wanting to go to college and not having the money for it.

Maria was college material—all her teachers said so. But her family not only couldn't afford to pay the tuition, they needed the income she could bring in from whatever work she could get. So Maria "knew" that college was out of the question—until she acted on a friend's suggestion and got a clerical job at a nearby college, where employees could go to school for free.

Looking back from the vantage point of her second semester, Maria says, "The real problem was that I was *afraid:* I didn't believe I could make it, so I couldn't find a way to do it."

Fear often keeps us from seeing clearly. As frightening as the problem is—having no money, for instance, or being addicted to a drug—the solution, whether seeking work or withdrawing from the drug, can seem equally frightening, though we may not admit it.

Just as everyone has problems, so everyone has fear. And usually, we come by that fear honestly. Maria, for instance, was the first person in her family to go to college, so why shouldn't she be afraid? Yet, just as we're told to stand on our own, we're told, "There's nothing to be afraid of."

This book will not tell you that. There's *plenty* to be afraid of. The trick is to let go of that fear long enough to be able to admit that there is a problem and see the possibility of a way out. All Maria had to do was to be willing to take her friend's suggestion—and now she is in college, doing what she thought she couldn't manage and what she secretly feared.

Fear can add to our problems in other ways, as well.

Just as we tend to convince ourselves that nobody else faces troubles like ours, we are afraid that anyone we ask for help will laugh at us or reject us. We fear embarrassment—and it *is* possible to "die of embarrassment," especially if you face a dangerous problem like abuse, addiction, or disease. You need to know that organizations like those listed in this book exist only because tens of thousands of people have difficulties like yours. The people who provide the help have heard enough painful stories to know that yours is *not* a laughing matter.

And often, no matter how dangerous or "impossible" are our problems, what looms even larger in our minds than the problem itself is the fear that other people will find out about it. Especially great for young people is the fear that their parents will find out. You need to know that you can get help that is confidential—help that only you and the provider know about. This book tells you how to seek help and information while maintaining your privacy and how to be sure that the service provided will stay private.

• • •

Once you are aware of the ways in which fear, like denial and isolation, can act to block you from the help that is available, you can put the fear aside just long enough to ask for help. But where to turn?

Maria was fortunate to have a friend with a good idea. But these days few individuals, whether family, friends, or teachers, can provide expert guidance through all of life's crises and challenges. This book shows you how to find the experts who *can.* It will tell you where to look, what to ask and expect, and how to evaluate what you're told. There are just a few more things you need to know first.

WHAT YOU NEED TO KNOW

- You need to know that you need help; and you've shown that by picking up this book.
- You need to know as clearly as possible what your problem is. If that seems confusing, go through the topics outlined in the contents, and then go back over those pressure points and symptoms listed earlier in this chapter.
- You need to know that *you have a right to get help*. Many young people believe that they're not entitled to help, simply because they are young. Also, they may have learned too well the lesson that once they've "made their bed" they deserve to "lie in it." Besides that, the adults around them, whether parents, teachers, or police, seem so powerful that seeking help for themselves seems pointless.

  It's for those reasons—the sense of powerlessness shared by the young and the image of power wielded by adults—that our system *does* give rights to young people. A discussion of those rights begins on page 111. For now, remember that you are entitled to health, safety, education, and support—and to the help you need to get those essentials.

- You need to know that help is available—help that you can receive directly and at no cost and without anyone else having to know. That's what the rest of this book is about: how to contact available help.

  You may be surprised to see how many places there are for a young person with troubles to turn. For though you may have some very grown-up problems, as a teenager, you may feel you're too young to seek help from grown-up sources. That might once have been true, but not today. Luckily, because of all the difficult problems young people face, more solutions are available than ever before. The sources for your solutions are listed in the next chapter.
- You need to know how to CONNECT—to ask for help—and that's hard. To start, go back to the beginning of the chapter. Instead of "I can do it *myself*!" try saying, "I don't have to handle this myself." For "*Nobody's* ever been in a mess like this!" say, "I deserve better than this." For "But you don't understand . . ." try, "Maybe there's somebody out there who knows what I'm feeling."

  And instead of "I'm FINE!" how about, "I need help." When you ask, in the right place, you will GET HELP.

In Chapter Three, you'll find detailed suggestions on what to ask, what to say, and what to do to make the best use of the help you get when you ask.

How to help yourself? Begin by turning the page.

CHAPTER TWO

WHERE TO FIND HELP

▲■▲■▲■▲■▲■▲■▲■▲■▲■▲■▲■▲■▲■▲■

HOW TO USE THIS BOOK TO GET HELP

You can find help for whatever problem you may have.

In the following pages, you'll find a baker's dozen of the most common difficulties teenagers face, listed in alphabetical order from "abuse" through "work." Within each category is detailed information about specific resources for help, for information, or for both. You'll also find suggestions on how to find additional resources—those that are in your community or those that exist to serve special problems that aren't included in these rather general topics.

Each of the resources listed here provides *free*, or nearly free, services, material, or referrals, and provides them to young people. Where costs are involved, or where rules limit what help a minor may receive, the entry notes it. For most of these resources, as you will see, you need not even identify yourself in order to receive the kind of service the group can offer.

This chapter lists two kinds of resources.

Those marked with a ▲ offer some kind of *direct* help, either by phone or in person. They also can provide information on and answer questions about the problems that they deal with. These groups and their services are described in detail so that you will have a good idea of what kind of direct help to expect before you ask.

Those marked with a ■ can point the way to more direct help. They provide: *information* about the problem, based on research they have gathered; *referral* to agencies that can serve your needs; and, in some cases, *"advocacy"*—lobbying and campaigning the public, press, and lawmakers toward achieving general solutions to the problems they address. They may be *clearinghouses* that simply collect up-to-date information and make it available to others, or they may perform all these functions. In any case, these entries are less detailed, because your contact with these groups is a first step toward finding a more specific solution to your problem.

Each of the following categories is organized like this: an introduction describes the problem and discusses some reasons why it may be hard—and why it is important—for people to ask for help with that particular difficulty.

Under the heading "Contact" is a list of the organizations that provide young people with help for the problem. Each organization is described, with an outline of the type of help it offers. You can get in touch with the groups through the address or the phone number listed for each. (Toll-free 800 numbers are included for those groups that have them.) If you write, it's a good idea to include a large, self-addressed, stamped envelope (SASE). If you phone, you may want to jot down your questions beforehand.

In the "Connect" portion of each category, you will find suggestions of what to say when you get in touch with the helping organizations that seem best for you.

The examples given under the heading "Get Help" will give you an idea of what to expect when you connect with the helping services listed.

Finally, "More Help" suggests other resources, especially those at a local level, where you can find assistance.

If you follow the steps outlined in each category, you will probably find it almost easy to get help in solving even the most difficult problem.

Although these listings represent a thorough collection of nationally recognized organizations, you will not, of course, find here *every* group or agency that exists to serve your needs because there are thousands, even tens of thousands, of them around the country, in every state and community. (The "Backup" chapter at the end of the book lists toll-free numbers, hotlines, and reading matter you can turn to for additional help.)

In "What to Ask," which begins on page 103, there are detailed tips on how to rate any service you contact and how best to get the help you need from it.

To use these listings sections, simply find the topic that most nearly matches your concerns, read about the agencies that can offer help, decide which to *contact,* and read how to *connect* and *get help*.

ABUSE

Abuse can take many forms. The most obvious is physical—violence, beatings, even torture. Mental and verbal abuse can be just as painful, when words or silence or bizarre behavior belittles or bewilders an individual. And violence directed at someone close to you makes you a victim, too. Sexual abuse makes headlines when it's uncovered; and when it's not, incest or any kind of forced intimacy can be a family's or a person's most agonizing secret, leaving scars that are unseen but very real. Neglect or simple nonresponse is a form of abuse, as well, making the victim feel worthless or "invisible." Parents can inflict abuse; so can teachers—or anyone else who has power over a younger or more dependent person. The causes for abuse are complex. But whatever its explanation or its form, you do not have to endure it or allow it to continue.

Remember that the abuser needs help as desperately as does the victim; anyone who willfully picks on a child (or other weaker, dependent person) is deeply troubled and was also very likely the victim of abuse. Remember, too, that you are not alone; close to 2 million cases of "child" abuse (one-quarter involve teenagers) are reported in the United States each year, and experts estimate that most cases are not reported.

Asking for help in abusive situations can be especially hard. Many victims feel a protective loyalty toward their abuser, especially within a family; or the abuser may threaten the victim with worse abuse if the secret is revealed. And when we see or suspect abuse directed at another family member or a friend, it can be very hard not to say "it's none of my business."

The helping resources listed here know all that: they know how hard it is. They also know about all the forms of abuse; nothing you can say will surprise or disgust them or scare them away, and they can tell you whether what you experience or observe is abuse. It *is* their "business" to help—to help the abuser and to help the victim—and they know how. All it takes to get advice or help is a phone call.

But IN AN EMERGENCY—when you or someone else is being assaulted or is in immediate danger—call the operator, the police, or your local emergency number (Operator or 911) and report your name, your location, and the situation so that rescuers can reach the scene right away! Lives are on the line.

To solve the problems in your life that are related to Abuse:

CONTACT

▲ *Sources marked with this symbol will provide direct help for your problem.*

■ *Sources marked with this symbol will provide information and/or referral that will help with your problem.*

▲ Childhelp USA

6463 Independence Avenue
Woodland Hills, CA 91367
(818) 347-7280

A national nonprofit charity combating child abuse in any of its forms—physical, emotional, and sexual—through treatment, prevention, and research. Childhelp provides child protection and family therapy directly in some cases and in every case offers free information, advice, or referral. If you are not sure whether the problem you see or experience is abuse, get in touch with Childhelp anyway for information that can help you decide.

■ Committee for Children

172 20th Avenue
Seattle, WA 98122
(206) 322-5050

A lobbying group for children's rights that maintains a clearinghouse of information on child-abuse laws.

■ C. Henry Kemp Center for the Prevention and Treatment of Child Abuse and Neglect

1205 Oneida Street
Denver, CO 80220
(303) 321-3963

A resource center that can provide information about regional agencies offering help for child abuse and its aftereffects.

■ National Center on Child Abuse and Neglect

Children's Bureau
U.S. Department of Health and Human Services
P.O. Box 1182
Washington, DC 20013
(703) 821-2086

A government clearinghouse for information and services concerning all forms of abuse. Contact the center for free information about the problem and local helping agencies.

■ National Coalition Against Domestic Violence

1000 16th Street, NW
Washington, DC 20036
1-800-333-7233

A national private organization whose member-groups operate shelters for victims of family violence. Contact the coalition for information about shelters in your area.

■ National Committee for Prevention of Child Abuse

332 South Michigan Avenue
Chicago, IL 60604
(312) 663-3520

A national, nonprofit network of professional and volunteer groups whose mission is to prevent child abuse through education, information, advocacy, and treatment. Contact the committee for information about the problem you are having and about how to find help for it.

■ National Council on Child Abuse and Family Violence

1155 Connecticut Avenue, NW
Washington, DC 20036
(202) 429-6695

6033 West Century Boulevard
Los Angeles, CA 90045
(213) 641-0311
Hotline: 1-800-222-2000

A national, nonprofit organization that promotes research into and awareness of child abuse and other forms of family violence and that assists in the activities of local and regional anti-abuse groups. Contact the council for information about abuse and about how to get help.

■ National Resource Center for Child Abuse and Neglect

American Humane Association–American
Association for Protecting Children
9725 East Hampden Avenue
Denver, CO 80231
(303) 695-0811

An umbrella organization for groups working against child abuse. It can provide names of child-protection organizations within your area.

▲ Parents Anonymous

6733 South Sepulveda Boulevard
Los Angeles, CA 90045
(213) 410-9732 or
1-800-421-0353 [CA: 1-800-356-0386]

An international nonprofit organization committed to the treatment and prevention of child abuse through peer-led, professionally facilitated self-help groups, free weekly support-group meetings, and a telephone network for troubled parents, and through separate services for children of violent families. Its toll-free phone number provides free information, guidance, and referrals.

Parents Anonymous has local groups nationwide and in Canada and Europe. In addition to contacting the national office, you can find local groups by calling the 800 number.

CONNECT

Remember: When you connect by phone, you can get help without revealing your identity, if you like.

When you connect by mail, you must *give your name and address (including ZIP code) in order to receive help—and a large SASE will speed the response.*

When you make contact with an agency that helps solve problems of abuse, you do not have to tell your whole story at once, and you don't have to worry about getting anyone in trouble.

You can say, for instance:

"I think my parent gets too angry. What can I do?" or,

"I am having a problem with my [mother, father, teacher, whomever]. If I tell you about it, what happens?" or,

"I think that my [neighbor, friend] is being abused" or, just

"I would like some information about child abuse."

You do not have to give your name. However, in order to provide much help, the counselor may need to know something about you.

GET HELP

The first kind of help that you will get when you connect with any of the agencies listed here is the sense that you are not alone. As you read literature that you receive or as you begin to talk with someone, you will learn that others have shared experiences similar to yours—and have found help. That, in itself, can give you a very good feeling.

But there's more, of course. You can get assistance for your specific problem just by phoning one of the helping or referral agencies listed here.

If you call Childhelp, for instance, here's what to expect:

The person answering the phone is a trained counselor who understands the pain of child abuse for all concerned and who is expert in helping to resolve a crisis. Once you (with the counselor's help, if you need it) have explained your situation, the counselor will find the name of the agency in your community best suited to dealing with it—and, in most cases, will put you directly in touch with that agency and stay on the line until you are connected. The counselor will also give you advice and suggestions on how to handle the situation right *now*.

Much of the long-term help for abusive situations, however, comes through talking out your experiences with groups of other people, usually in the presence of a professionally trained counselor.

When you connect with Parents Anonymous, for instance, the person at the other end of the phone will have personal or professional experience with the kind of family violence that hurts children. Depending on the situation you describe, you will be told where and how to get immediate help in your community, and you can be put in touch with someone nearby with whom you can talk out your worries. If you or your parent decides to go to a (free) local group meeting, there will be other people there who share your experiences and who get help from each other and from a professionally trained expert. No one *ever* needs to know your last name or your full identity, and you will not be required to take legal or other official action.

MORE HELP

Every state government has an office for the prevention and treatment of child abuse, and many county and local governments do, too. In addition, many private social service organizations provide community services concerning family violence. To find the ones near you, look for them by name in the white pages or "Government" section of your phone book or under "Social Service Organizations" in your local yellow pages.

Some of them are the following:

Department of Child Protective Services
Department of Social Services
Bureau of Child Welfare
Bureau of Children and Family Services
Big Brothers/Big Sisters of America
Salvation Army
Volunteers of America

Remember that when you phone, you need not give your name.

See also: For help in dealing with abuse or other personal violence *before* it reaches such a critical stage, see also the sections on "Addiction and Alcoholism" (pages 22–29) and "Family Crises" (pages 55–64).

ADDICTION AND ALCOHOLISM

No one is "too young" to be addicted to alcohol or other drugs, and for many teens, these chemicals are the *cause* of many of their overwhelming and seemingly unrelated problems. If it's possible that they are a problem for you—interfering with school life, eating up funds, or causing trouble with family, friends, or the law—and you find you can't "just say no" even when you want to, you may not be dealing with just a bad habit. You may have a disease for which you can get help from the following *free* sources (which can also help if someone close to you seems to have a problem with alcohol or other drugs). With no questions asked or records kept, they can provide information (including the "warning signs" of addiction), refer you to special treatments if necessary, and offer you a way to solve the problem right now.

But IN AN EMERGENCY—when faced with danger from a drug or alcohol overdose—call your local emergency number (Operator or 911), or call an ambulance or rescue squad *immediately.*

To solve the problems in your life that are related to Addiction and Alcoholism:

CONTACT

▲ *Sources marked with this symbol will provide direct help for your problem.*

■ *Sources marked with this symbol will provide information and/or referral that will help with your problem.*

▲ Alcoholics Anonymous

Box 459, Grand Central Station
New York, NY 10163
(212) 686-1100

A nonprofit, nonsectarian self-help fellowship of people who meet regularly to share their experiences as a way of staying sober and helping others to solve their problems with alcohol. Though not a medical treatment, AA's successful approach to the disease of alcoholism is acknowledged by the medical profession. There are no dues, fees, or costs of any kind, and no membership requirements other than a desire to stop drinking. AA is open to any age, with special groups for young people in many communities.

Alcoholics Anonymous has local networks nationwide and internationally. In addition to contacting the national office, you can find local chapters listed in the white pages of your phone book under "AA" or "Alcoholics Anonymous" or in the yellow pages under "Alcohol."

▲ For Cocaine Abuse

Hotline: 1-800-COCAINE

Recovery groups and treatment programs for cocaine abusers are not as widespread or uniform as Alcoholics Anonymous or

Narcotics Anonymous, but free or low-cost help is available in most communities. To find out where or to get other information about the drug, call the cocaine hotline listed above. This is a round-the-clock information and referral service based at a New Jersey hospital and manned by trained counselors who are former cocaine users. They can answer your questions and direct you to treatment.

▲ Gamblers Anonymous (GA)

P.O. Box 17173
Los Angeles, CA 90017
(213) 386-8789

A nonprofit self-help recovery program for compulsive gamblers, based on the principles and techniques of Alcoholics Anonymous (see page 23) but not affiliated with it. Although compulsive gambling does not seem to be as prevalent among young people as other addictions, signs of the compulsion may be present early. You can get information about them by contacting GA.

Gamblers Anonymous has local groups nationwide. In addition to contacting the national office, you can find local groups listed in the white pages of your phone book under "Gamblers Anonymous."

▲ Narcotics Anonymous (NA)

P.O. Box 9999
Van Nuys, CA 91409
(818) 780-3951

A nonprofit, nonsectarian program of self-help for people for whom drugs have become a major problem. NA's successful program of recovery, which focuses on the disease of *addiction* rather than on any single substance, is based in principle upon that of Alcoholics Anonymous (see page 23), though the groups are not affiliated. Members meet regularly and remain in contact with each other in order to stay away from drugs and learn to enjoy life without them. There are no dues, fees, or costs of any kind and no membership requirement other than the desire to stop using narcotics. A great many of NA's members are young people.

Narcotics Anonymous has local groups nationwide and internationally. In addition to contacting the national office, you can find local groups listed in the white pages of your phone book under "Narcotics Anonymous."

■ National Clearinghouse for Alcohol and Drug Information

P.O. Box 2345
Rockville, MD 20852
(301) 468-2600

A government agency that provides facts on all aspects of drugs, alcohol, and addictive diseases.

■ National Council on Alcoholism

12 West 21st Street
New York, NY 10010
(212) 206-6770 or 1-800-NCA-CALL

A private association of professionals that provides free information, publications, and referrals on alcoholism, its symptoms, and its treatment.

▲ Potsmokers Anonymous

316 East Third Street
New York, NY 10009
(212) 254-1777

A much smaller and more localized group than the other addiction-recovery programs listed in this section. It focuses on education, but it also coordinates support meetings. Contact the group for meeting locations, information, and suggestions about where to turn if you think you may have a problem with marijuana.

■ PRIDE Drug Info Hotline

1-800-241-7946

When dialed from a touch-tone phone, this number, sponsored by a national group of concerned parents, provides taped information on a wide variety of topics related to drug and alcohol abuse, including symptoms of addiction and resources for treatment. Available from 5:00 P.M. to 8:30 A.M. (Eastern Standard Time) on week-nights and all day on weekends.

CONNECT

Remember: When you connect by phone, you can get help without revealing your identity, if you like.

When you connect by mail, you must *give your name and address (including ZIP code) in order to receive help—and a large SASE will speed the response.*

When you make contact with any of these organizations, you do not have to give any details about whatever concerns you may have. Many of the callers who seek information and advice don't know whether they (or someone close to them) have an addiction problem or not.

If you telephone, you can say simply:

"I would like some information about your organization" [or "about alcoholism" or "about addiction"]. or,

"How do you tell if you have a drug problem?" or,

"Can a teenager be an alcoholic?" or even,

"I have a friend who may have a problem with alcohol [or drugs]."

The person at the other end of the phone will help you with the rest of the conversation.

When you write, you can simply say, "Please send me information about what your organization does, including the locations of any assistance centers in my area."

If you write to any of the "Anonymous" groups, they will send information in a *plain* envelope, and your name won't be put on any kind of mailing list. If you are concerned for your privacy when you write, you can request that the material come in an unmarked package.

Connecting with these groups doesn't mean that you are making any kind of statement or commitment, but it's an important step toward helping you feel better.

GET HELP

The kind of help you get depends, of course, upon which kind of group you select from the list. An information service will provide facts about addiction or alcoholism and will suggest the helping agencies you might contact in your area.

When you phone one of the hotlines, you will be talking either with a professional counselor experienced in treating addictions or with someone who has learned firsthand that chemical dependencies can be broken. You'll get information about the symptoms of addiction and about how it is treated.

From the helping organizations, you'll also gain the reassuring sense that *many* people have problems with drugs or alcohol for which they have found solutions.

What you will *not* get from *any* of these organizations, whether you write or phone, is any effort to force you (or anyone else) to treat an addiction or alcoholism problem. Instead, you'll get facts to help you decide for yourself what your next step should be.

When you connect with AA or NA, for example, here's what you can expect:

Your phone call will be answered by an AA or NA member who once had the same questions and worries as you do and thus can respond from personal experience. You needn't identify yourself, and you will be given the times and places of groups that meet near to you or, *if you choose*, someone close to your own age can phone or visit you for a conversation in greater depth. If you attend a group meeting, that's all you have to do—go. You won't have to say anything, do anything, sign anything, or even make yourself known to anyone. Whether you think you have a problem or not, you can find out what it's about by picking up some of the pamphlets that may be available there or just by listening as the people in the room take turns talking about the improvements that freedom from addictions has made in their lives. And if you decide to try a meeting, it's perfectly all right to take someone with you.

MORE HELP

If for some reason you don't feel right getting in touch with any of these organizations, you may feel more comfortable talking out your worries with someone closer to you—a doctor, member of the clergy, teacher, or coach. Addictions are such complex problems, though, that your best help will come from someone with either professional or personal experience. Besides, you can still turn to those closer to you for moral support. Or keep your eyes open for people you know who used to abuse drink and drugs and now don't; ask them how they did it.

But whatever you do, don't close your eyes to a problem that you think may exist. Addiction isn't just a socially unacceptable bad habit: it kills.

See also: It's reported that one of every three people in the United States, even those not addicted to alcohol or other drugs, is affected by alcoholism or other addictions. If the addictive disease of a family member or close friend makes your life miserable, you can't "cure" him or her, but you *can* get free help for yourself from organizations like **Al-Anon Family Groups; Alateen; Families Anonymous; Gam-Anon;** or **Nar-Anon.** These and others are listed in detail in the section on "Family Crises" (pages 55–64).

ADOPTION

"I'm adopted" is an answer that some people give to the question, "What's your problem?" For some of the tens of thousands of young Americans who are adopted, it *is* a problem. Their adoptive family may be abusive, they may feel uncomfortable about being "different" from them, or they may have discovered the truth of their birth in a sudden or unpleasant way.

Or an adoptee may simply be curious about his or her origins. This is quite natural, especially (but not exclusively) for teenagers, since adolescence is a time when most people, adopted or not, are busy discovering who they are. Today, laws and customs make it easier than it once was for adoptees to trace their birth parents, but it's still not simple—and there are factors besides rules and regulations to consider carefully in deciding whether and how to embark on a search. You and your family may simply need professional guidance in working out whatever problems exist in your present life.

By following the suggestions included here, you can seek your birth parents, find support to ease whatever discomfort you may feel, or both.

To solve the problems in your life that are related to Adoption:

CONTACT

▲ *Sources marked with this symbol will provide direct help for your problem.*

■ *Sources marked with this symbol will provide information and/or referral that will help with your problem.*

▲ ALMA Society

P.O. Box 154, Washington Bridge Station
New York, NY 10033
(212) 581-1568

A private group whose members include many thousands of adoptees and adoptive parents around the country. The society's primary purpose is to facilitate the reunions of adopted children with their natural parents (ALMA stands for Adoptees' Liberty Movement Association), although other ALMA activities include conferences and workshops on adoptions and reunions. Membership is open to those aged 18 and over; registration requires a moderate fee, but people of any age can participate in support activities.

ALMA Society has local groups nationwide. In addition to contacting the national office, you can find local groups listed in the white pages of your phone book under "ALMA Society."

■ OURS

3307 Highway 100 North
Minneapolis, MN 55422
(612) 535-4829

A free self-help network that provides support and information for people in adoptive families. Local groups offer a setting for discussion and advice.

OURS has local groups nationwide. To locate a nearby group, phone or send a self-addressed stamped envelope to the main office.

CONNECT

Remember: *When you connect by phone, you can get help without revealing your identity, if you like.*

When you connect by mail, you must *give your name and address (including ZIP code) in order to receive help—and a large SASE will speed the response.*

When you connect with groups or agencies that provide help or information about adoption, say:

"I am __________ years old and live in _______________. I'm adopted [or "I think that I'm adopted"], and I would like to know what your organization does."

Think ahead about what else you want to know, such as:

"How do I find my birth family?"

"What are the rules in my state that affect me?"

"Do other people my age feel this way: [describe way] about being adopted?"

"How can I find other people in my area who are adopted and who may be having experiences like mine?"

GET HELP

When you ask for help from these groups (or from an agency), you may not be able to get help in searching for your birth parents right away: you may be too young or the state where you live may have restrictive rules. But at the very least you will get information, advice, and support from someone who is familiar with situations like yours and who knows what questions to ask so that you can focus on the problems you really want to solve.

No matter what your age or your goals, you can get facts about adoption, be put on a mailing list for information, and find some groups where you will be able to talk with other adoptees and learn about their experiences and feelings. If you decide to pursue a search for your natural parents and are old enough, you will be guided through the process of registration and search, depending on your situation and the state in which you were adopted.

There are some important cautions and suggestions to consider, though:

Issues related to adoption can be heavily emotional for all concerned—adoptees, birth parents, and adoptive parents alike—so proceed with an awareness of this. For this reason, too, "searchers" are easy victims for fraud. Check thoroughly any group or individual who promises to find your roots, especially if a large fee is required!

MORE HELP

Adoptees have other resources for direct help and advice:

If you were adopted through a **private agency**, you can go there or you can locate the **lawyer** or other individual who arranged the adoption if yours was a private placement.

Or you can go directly to the **court** through which you were adopted or contact the **government agency** in your state (usually within a department of social services) that regulates and records adoptions.

Policies and laws on adoption vary widely according to locality, and they are currently in a process of change. If you are unsure about the rules and your rights, contact the **Civil Liberties Union** (see page 71).

Try to talk with other people—adults as well as teens—who have experience with adoption. You may not have to find a formal network to do this; just ask around. Sometimes, the simple act of talking with another person can clear your mind about what you want to do.

See also: If you are anxious to find your birth parents because your adoptive home is unhappy, it may be wiser to resolve your current situation before searching out some ideal parent who, in your fantasies, would have treated you better. For help with trouble at home, see also the sections on "Abuse" (pages 13–21) and "Family Crises" (pages 55–64).

DISABILITIES

Until recently, people with disabilities were handicapped, blocked from what they wanted to do in life. Today, things are different; in fact, a great deal of special help is available so that people with difficult physical conditions not only can cope successfully and independently with life, but also can achieve accomplishments equal to those of the able-bodied. The organizations and other suggestions included in this section provide some of that help.

Still, if you live with a disability, you may have a particularly hard time asking for help. You may have been taught to believe that little is possible for you. You may feel that you don't "deserve" help. Or other feelings, like fear and anger, may prevent you from trying. But it's worth following up on some of the suggestions here, because the people who provide the help understand these feelings—often from their own personal experience.

The people who provide the help also understand the feelings of an able-bodied family member who lives with a disabled person. If you have a brother, sister, or parent who is handicapped, you (and the rest of the family) can benefit from counseling and guidance offered or suggested by these specialists in helping the disabled to cope.

To solve the problems in your life that are related to Disabilities:

CONTACT

▲ *Sources marked with this symbol will provide direct help for your problem.*

■ *Sources marked with this symbol will provide information and/or referral that will help with your problem.*

■ Association for Children and Adults with Learning Disabilities

4156 Library Road
Pittsburgh, PA 15234
(412) 341-1515

A group of professionals and other concerned individuals that provides information on sources for appropriate treatment of a wide variety of learning problems and that can refer you to one of its state branches for more detailed help.

■ Center for Independent Living

2539 Telegraph Avenue
Berkeley, CA 94704
(415) 841-4776

An organization of and for the disabled, providing information, advice, and referrals on practical aids and personal techniques that enhance the ability for living independently.

■ Coordinating Council for Handicapped Children

20 East Jackson Street
Chicago, IL 60604
(312) 939-3513

A private umbrella organization for groups working to aid disabled young people. It answers phone and mail requests for information and assistance about educational and other services available in local areas for children and youth with disabilities.

■ Higher Education and the Handicapped

One Dupont Circle, NW
Washington, DC 20036
1-800-544-3284

A resource center concerned with higher education and training for people with disabilities.

▲ National Easter Seal Society

2023 West Ogden Avenue
Chicago, IL 60612
(312) 243-8400
(312) 243-8880 for the hearing-impaired

A nonprofit, voluntary agency that provides direct services to people with disabilities. Individuals of all ages having disabilities resulting from any cause can find assistance through Easter Seal programs that provide them with or direct them to resources to help them develop their abilities and live purposeful lives.

The National Easter Seal Society has state and regional societies nationwide. In addition to contacting the national office, you can find local offices listed in the white pages of your phone book under "Easter Seal."

■ National Information Center for Handicapped Children and Youth

P.O. Box 1492
Washington, DC 20013
(703) 893-6061

An agency that offers free information on and referrals to resources of all sorts for students and other young people with disabilities.

■ National Resource Institute on Children with Handicaps

Child Development Center
University of Washington
Seattle, WA 98195
(206) 545-1350

A professional association that provides the public with research results and offers guidance to special services.

■ Self-Help Clearinghouse

Saint Claires–Riverside Medical Center
Denville, NJ 07834
(201) 625-7101 or 1-800-367-6274

A privately run center that compiles and maintains the *Self-Help Sourcebook*, an extremely valuable guide to self-help groups around the country in which people with disabilities and other life problems provide mutual support for one another. The organization lists (and updates) well over 100 helplines that you can call and keeps lists of groups that provide support for even the rarest of disorders that disable people of all ages. Call or write for a copy of the book, which costs about $9.00, or to get referrals to a group of people who share your disability.

■ World Institute on Disability

1720 Oregon Street
Berkeley, CA 94703
(415) 486-8314

A policy and resource center founded by and for the disabled, to promote independent living. It provides information as well as referrals to attendant services.

CONNECT

Remember: When you connect by phone, you can get help without revealing your identity, if you like.

When you connect by mail, you must *give your name and address (including ZIP code) in order to receive help—and a large SASE will speed the response.*

When you connect with an agency that provides help for the disabled, say:

"I have ______________. I live in ______________, and I am ______________ years old. Where can I get some help?" or,

"I need some information about ______________." or,

"If a person has ______________, what kind of help can he or she get?"

Think about the kinds of help that you might want:

- Information about your disability (or that in your family)
- Help with finding mobility or coping assistance

- Therapy or treatment for the condition
- Contact and support from others in your situation
- Legal or advocacy assistance toward receiving the treatment, education, or other rights you deserve
- Any other resources this agency can suggest

You will also want to know the *cost,* if any, of this help and the *location* of it, since these factors will help you decide where to turn.

GET HELP

When you seek help for dealing with a disability, the specific response you get depends, of course, upon the details of your situation. From the Easter Seal Society, for example, you will learn where you—and your family, if necessary—can get a professional evaluation of your needs and where in your area (for free, if you can't pay) you can find help. Among the direct services provided by professional associations like the Easter Seal Society are the following: physical, occupational, and speech therapies; vocational training; special recreation; and psychological counseling.

When you connect with a self-help support group, you will be told how to contact people very much like yourself in your area or you will be given a toll-free number to call for the information. Membership in these groups is free and open to all ages. Although they do not provide medical treatment, they offer something that's crucial in a different way: sharing experiences with someone in a similar situation. Next to necessary physical or medical assistance, that can be a very positive action, and members of such groups form, in themselves, a network of information about how to make the most of their—and your—abilities.

The people who respond to your request at any of these organizations are either disabled themselves or have wide experience in dealing with the problems and challenges of disabilities, so they understand your feelings and your need for the same kind of mobility and opportunity that everyone else enjoys.

MORE HELP

Help is also available through your **doctor** or **hospital**, of course, and your **school** system is also likely to have special services that you can use; all you need to do is ask.

In your city, state, or county, you will likely find **nonprofit organizations** like the Lighthouse for the Blind, the Society for the Deaf, and others that can give help for specific disabilities. (If it's not a group that's widely known or if it is one to which you haven't been referred by a trusted professional, be sure to check its credentials first.)

These organizations can also put you in touch with **animal companion training schools**—schools for guide dogs to lead the blind, hearing-ear dogs to help the hearing-impaired, and service dogs to aid the wheelchair-bound.

Federal law requires that any institution receiving federal funds (and that means almost all of them) be accessible to the disabled, and many local governments have accessibility laws, as well. So if you are ever turned away from an opportunity, you have the right to fight—and you can get help for that, too.

See also: The entries under "Health Care" (pages 65–69) may also be useful. Because disabilities can cause tensions in the household, see "Family Crises" (pages 55–64). If help is needed in receiving rights as a handicapped person, see "Legal Matters" (pages 70–75).

EATING DISORDERS

Not too long ago, if someone had what was called an eating problem, it meant simply that he or she was a "picky eater" or "fat." Today, eating disorders are recognized as serious health problems. They are particularly common among teenagers, and they can be especially dangerous for teens. Anorexia nervosa, bulimia, compulsive overeating, and compulsive dieting can ravage bodies and minds that are going through a critical and complex stage of development. These disorders may be symptoms of other troubles, and they can be deadly.

An estimated 6 million Americans suffer from eating disorders, so if you suspect that you might, you aren't alone. And it's likely that all of those millions considered their food compulsions to be deep and shameful secrets—so you're not alone in that regard, either. Many thousands have found help from the resources listed here, and you can, too.

To solve the problems in your life that are related to Eating Disorders:

CONTACT

▲ *Sources marked with this symbol will provide direct help for your problem.*

■ *Sources marked with this symbol will provide information and/or referral that will help with your problem.*

■ American Anorexia/Bulimia Association

133 Cedar Lane
Teaneck, NJ 07666
(201) 836-1800

An association of and for people with eating disorders, their families, and the professionals who work in the field. It provides information and referrals on the disorders and their treatment and can direct you to counseling and self-help groups in your area.

▲ Anorexia Nervosa and Related Disorders, Inc.

P.O. Box 7
Highland Park, IL 60035
(312) 831-3438

A national, nonprofit organization with local groups that hold self-help meetings with guidance from health professionals. It provides information on eating disorders and referrals to medical specialists.

Anorexia Nervosa and Related Disorders, Inc., has local groups in forty states and in Canada. In addition to contacting the national office, you can find local groups listed in the white pages of your phone book under "Anorexia Nervosa and Related Disorders, Inc."

▲ National Anorexic Aid Society, Inc.

5796 Karl Road
Columbus, OH 43229
(614) 436-1112

An organization that provides information and medical referrals for people with *all* eating disorders and for their families. Those who pay a small yearly membership fee can attend support groups and receive educational material.

▲ Overeaters Anonymous (OA)

P.O. Box 92870
Los Angeles, CA 90009
(213) 542-8363

A nonprofit self-help fellowship of people who meet regularly to share their experiences as a way of dealing with their compulsive overeating and other problems with food. OA is based on the principles of Alcoholics Anonymous (see page 23), and its members use AA-style techniques. It is not a medical treatment, and it stresses that it is "not a diet club"; rather, OA works on the proven premise that members ensure their own recovery by helping others with eating problems. Open to all concerned, at no cost.

Overeaters Anonymous has local chapters nationwide. In addition to contacting the national office, you can find local chapters listed in the white pages of your phone book under "Overeaters Anonymous."

CONNECT

Remember: When you connect by phone, you can get help without revealing your identity, if you like.

When you connect by mail, you must *give your name and address (including ZIP code) in order to receive help—and a large SASE will speed the response.*

When you seek help for anorexia, bulimia, compulsive overeating, or other eating problem, you can say:

"I am ______________ years old, and I think I have an eating problem. What should I do?" or,

"How do you know if you have an eating problem?" or,

"Are there any groups or specialists in my area where I could find out about eating problems?" or,

"Please send me information about eating disorders and how they are treated."

Because that's what you need to know: what it is, how it's treated, and how you can get the kind of help that you decide you need.

GET HELP

The kind of help you get with an eating problem does depend on the kind that you are willing to accept. When you connect with OA, for example, you will get information about the OA program and a list of the meeting times and places in your area. There are many special meetings for teenagers. If you decide to attend a meeting, you will find no "weigh-ins," no diet plans or pills, but a group of people like yourself who will listen to and understand your problems and will share their own experiences.

It's up to you to decide whether to follow their example. But keep in mind that anorexia and bulimia are potentially dangerous medical conditions that require special treatment. So if, based on the information you receive from any of the organizations listed here, you suspect that you may have a problem, you would be very wise to follow up by seeking medical attention.

Whether you get help from a professional or from another person like yourself, you will find, first of all, that you are not unique or alone.

MORE HELP

You can find information and help for eating problems from your **doctor, hospital,** or **youth clinic.** You will do best finding an *expert* helper, one who understands how serious and complex the problem is. Wherever you turn, the most important step is being able to acknowledge that you may have a problem and then to follow through with the treatment.

See also: Eating disorders are not minor problems, so under "Health Care" (pages 65–69), you'll find suggestions on medical treatment for eating disorders. The "Mental Health and Suicide" (pages 76–82) listings include resources for psychotherapy or emotional support.

EDUCATION AND SCHOLARSHIPS

"Everybody" knows that education beyond the basic minimum required by law is so expensive that no one can afford it except the very rich, the very smart, or the fortunate. But in this case, "everybody" is wrong. You and your family—even your teachers and counselors—may read and hear so much about the costs of college and special schools that it's natural to assume you can't afford the kind of education you'd really like to have, especially if you don't have high grades or test scores. So you may just give up and settle for a dead-end future—and that would be a mistake.

The real facts are that you *can* afford to get as much of an advanced education as you can handle. It's true: you just have to ask for help in the right places. The organizations listed in this section can give you advice and information about financial aid of all sorts and guidance in finding the kind of schooling you can fit into your life. You'll also find other suggestions here on ways to get free or low-cost education to meet your needs. You might not end up going to school exactly when or where you'd most like to, but you'll be surprised at the variety of possibilities that are open to you.

So don't give up on yourself. Check out all of your educational options. And don't wait! Many aid programs require application long before the start of a college career. On the other hand, don't assume that if you're already out of school, you're out of luck: plenty of programs are available for potential students of every age and status.

To solve the problems in your life that are related to Education:

CONTACT

▲ *Sources marked with this symbol will provide direct help for your problem.*

■ *Sources marked with this symbol will provide information and/or referral that will help with your problem.*

■ Citizens' Scholarship Foundation of America

1505 Riverview Road
St. Peter, MN 56082
(507) 931-1682

A national, nonprofit student-aid service organization whose goal is to expand access to higher education. It works to encourage corporations and communities to donate money for college scholarships and then manages those scholarship programs. In addition to the corporate and association programs that it manages, CSFA sponsors the **Dollars for Scholars** foundations through which communities can raise money for scholarship aid.

■ The College Board

45 Columbus Avenue
New York, NY 10023
(212) 713-8000

A national, nonprofit organization with more than 2,500 member educational institutions and associations whose purpose is to help students make the transition from high school into college and increase their access to higher education through such services as guidance, testing, and financial aid. It will send free publications that provide information and guidance on college admission and financial aid, and it can also refer you to a regional office for help that focuses on your area.

■ National Commission for Cooperative Education

360 Huntington Avenue
Boston, MA 02115
(617) 437-3778

An organization that encourages and helps to coordinate cooperative education programs in some 900 colleges across the country that allow about 200,000 students to take time during their schooling to work off-campus for one of 50,000 participating employers.

■ U.S. Department of Education

Office of Student Financial Assistance
400 Maryland Avenue, SW
Washington, DC 20202
(202) 732-3391

The government agency that administers the federally funded financial aid—grants, loans, and work-study programs—which millions of students use to help pay their tuition. The office also publishes guides and other publications that provide information about sources of financial aid.

The Department of Education has 10 regional offices around the country. In addition to contacting the Washington office, you can find the regional offices listed in the "U.S. Government" section of your phone book.

■ United Student Aid Funds, Inc. (USA Funds, Inc.)

P.O. Box 50429
Indianapolis, IN 46250
(317) 849-6510 or 1-800-LOAN USA

A national, nonprofit financial services corporation that specializes in guaranteeing student loans. Since its founding in 1961, USA Funds has helped 2 million students finance higher education by underwriting the loans of people who otherwise would not be eligible.

CONNECT

Remember: When you connect by phone, you can get help without revealing your identity, if you like.

When you connect by mail, you must *give your name and address (including ZIP code) in order to receive help—and a large SASE will speed the response.*

To get help with financing your education, you can say to the resource organization:

"How do I reach the regional financial aid office and my state's office of student aid?" or,

"I'm a student in the ________ grade and I'd like information about college scholarship programs or loans or co-op programs." or,

"I'm a student in the ________ grade [or out of school ________ years]. What kind of information can you give me about college and scholarships?"

It's useful to have some idea in advance of the kind of schooling you want and the maximum amount you can spend. But try to clear your mind of any preconceived ideas about what's best for you or what's possible, because this is an area where being flexible can get you what you need. Remember, too, that if one organization can't help, ask for suggestions about others that might be able to.

GET HELP

The groups listed here will not *send* you money for education, of course, but they will help you greatly toward finding and receiving the financial help you need.

The help you will get from the U.S. Department of Education, for example, includes a free "Student Guide," updated yearly, which describes in detail federal financial aid programs and how to apply for them. It also tells you how to contact the appropriate office in your state and suggests other sources of information. Depending on your situation (eligibility rules are spelled out in the booklet), you may qualify for a grant, which you won't have to repay; college work-study, which will help you earn money for college; or a low-interest student loan, which you must pay back over time.

The Citizens' Scholarship Foundation does not give out money itself, but it will tell you where you can apply—sometimes in unexpected places—to be considered for privately funded or community-funded financial aid.

And The College Board, which students tend to think of as the source of all those standardized tests, also provides a variety of other services—publications that can help in selecting a college and in finding financial aid. Especially useful are their annual "College Planning Guide for Students" and "Meeting College Costs" booklets.

In short, if you research thoroughly and apply carefully, you *can* afford higher education.

MORE HELP

In addition to the sources listed in this section, be sure to check the following helpful resources:

- Your **school counselor's office.** In addition to the counselor, you'll find files full of information about schools as well as scholarships.
- Your **public library.** Ask the librarian where to find financial aid information and college directories as well as ERIC, a computerized guide to all aspects of education.
- The **financial aid offices** of any schools that interest you. You needn't feel intimidated by them; they're there to help.
- All **groups with which you have *any* connection:** your parents' employers, unions, or professional associations; community organizations (Chamber of Commerce, betterment societies, and the like) and any fraternal or service groups (Elks, American Legion, etc.) within your community; religious groups; clubs like 4-H and Scouts. Any or all of these may offer special scholarships, as do professional and vocational societies (the American Medical Association, for instance, or the Society of Civil Engineers) that want to encourage potential members. If you have any special skills—like athletics or music—be sure to look into special grants that you may apply for.
- The **military.** Don't overlook the armed services; a wide variety of education and training is provided for men and women who enlist. Just be sure you know what you're signing on for before you sign up!

- Your own **employer.** Many employers pay for employees' education. Find out if yours does, or find another one that does. Or see about getting a job at a college that provides free tuition for employees. Don't imagine that you must attend college full-time and be out before you're 22. Today, adult part-time students are almost in the majority on American campuses, and many colleges make it easy for you to go to school while you're holding a job.

Remember that there are well over 2,000 four-year colleges in the United States, not just the handful that most people can easily name, and tuition at state-run institutions is one-tenth that of private schools. So get some guidebooks, dig in the library files, and look! Also, the "pool" of potential students is growing smaller, so colleges are likely to go out of their way to let you in and find ways for you to pay.

If your grades or test scores aren't terrific, don't give up. Talk with counselors to find out what you can do to strengthen or make up for your weak points—perhaps by being tutored or by attending a special school. Consider enrolling at a two-year community college, where admissions policies tend to be liberal, and doing well enough to be eligible to complete your undergraduate work elsewhere. Or consider specialized career training rather than formal higher education—that may be just as valuable, and you can always attend college later, as many do.

But beware of:

- Signing any kind of loan document or enrollment agreement without fully understanding what it says.
- Training schools that "guarantee" you a job or financial aid; find out the facts for yourself before you sign up.
- Services that, for a fee, will "find" you finan-

> cial aid or "promise" you an acceptance. Some of these may be legitimate, but the service for which they charge you may be one that you can perform for yourself at no cost.

If you're smart enough, you can get the education you want—and often "smart" has more to do with finding an intelligent way to cope than with scoring high on tests.

FAMILY CRISES

We tend to imagine that everybody else's family is "normal"—that we're the only people on the block having trouble at home. The truth is, of course, that *every* family faces problems at one time or another. Sometimes, these problems are short-lived and specific—mourning a death, for instance, or coping with an accident or disaster. More often, trouble—dissension, disease, financial difficulty—is long-term or ongoing. Family problems like these almost always have a ripple effect: the crisis that afflicts one family member or one area of family life spreads to affect, in different ways, the whole group.

So the bad news is that if you have trouble in one corner of your home, *you* are likely to become troubled yourself, whether you realize it or not (see pages 4–5 for symptoms of stress).

The good news is that you can get help, easily and for little or no money. Sometimes, all you need is a sympathetic listener who has experience with similar problems. You'll find suggestions for that kind of help here, as well as ideas for finding other resources in your community. You can't solve the problem on your own—can't cure the disease or break the addiction or mend the marriage—and you shouldn't try. But you *can* get help for yourself.

The important news is that if you are living in a troubled household, you should find help in order to ward off future pain. Many family problems pass from generation to generation. You can break the cycle.

To solve the problems in your life that are related to Family Crises:

CONTACT

▲ *Sources marked with this symbol will provide direct help for your problem.*

■ *Sources marked with this symbol will provide information and/or referral that will help with your problem.*

▲ Al-Anon Family Groups/Alateen

1372 Broadway
New York, NY 10106
(212) 302-7240 or
1-800-356-9996 (outside of New York)

Al-Anon is a nonprofit, nonsectarian self-help fellowship of people whose lives have been affected by alcoholism in a family member or close friend. As an independent outgrowth of Alcoholics Anonymous (see page 23), it uses the same structure and approach to provide free help and information for families of alcoholics (whether or not the alcoholic is seeking help). Free Al-Anon meetings in every community are open to all. Al-Anon sponsors **Alateen**, with 3,000 support groups around the world for teenage relatives and friends of alcoholics. **Adult Children of Alcoholics (ACOA)**, also a part of Al-Anon, holds its own meetings but is primarily for people past the teen years.

Al-Anon Family Groups has local groups nationwide and internationally. In addition to contacting the national office, you can find local groups by calling the 800 number or by looking in the white pages of your phone book under "Al-Anon Family Groups."

▲ Compassionate Friends

Box 3696
Oak Brook, IL 60522
(312) 990-0010

A self-help association for parents and siblings of a child who has died. Members meet and talk over their experiences as a way of resolving grief and dealing with the practical problems they encounter as a result of the death.

Compassionate Friends has local groups nationwide. In addition to contacting the national office, you can find local groups listed in the white pages of your phone book under "Compassionate Friends."

▲ Families Anonymous

Box 528
Van Nuys, CA 91408
(818) 989-7841

A nonprofit self-help fellowship of relatives and friends of people who abuse drugs or exhibit related behavioral problems. Based on the principles of Alcoholics Anonymous (see page 23) but not affiliated with AA or Al-Anon, it holds free weekly discussion meetings where members share suggestions and emotional support.

Families Anonymous has local groups in most states. In addition to contacting the national office, you can find local groups listed in the white pages of your phone book under "Families Anonymous."

■ Family Resource Coalition

230 North Michigan Avenue
Chicago, IL 60601
(312) 726-4750

A national network of community-based programs that develop family strengths. Its national service provides information about local programs for family education and support.

■ Family Service America

11700 West Lake Park Drive
Milwaukee, WI 53224
1-800-221-2681

A network of several hundred member agencies throughout the country that provide family counseling. Phone for referral to an agency in your area.

▲ Gamblers Anonymous

P.O. Box 17173
Los Angeles, CA 90017
(213) 386-8789

Gam-Anon

P.O. Box 157
Whitestone, NY 11357
(718) 352-1671

Two national, nonprofit self-help groups in which people focus on recovery from compulsive gambling. They are unaffiliated outgrowths of Alcoholics Anonymous and Al-Anon (see pages 23 and 56) and use the same principles and techniques. Gam-Anon's members are the families and friends of compulsive gamblers who seek to understand the gambling addiction and to help themselves.

Gamblers Anonymous and Gam-Anon have local groups nationwide. In addition to contacting the national offices, you can find local groups listed in the white pages of your phone book under "Gamblers Anonymous" and "Gam-Anon."

■ National Association for Children of Alcoholics

31582 Coast Highway
South Laguna, CA 92677
(714) 499-3889

A national nonprofit organization that serves as a resource for the children of alcoholics. From it, you can get publications and other information about alcoholism and alcoholic families, as well as suggestions and referrals to sources of direct help.

■ National Council on Child Abuse & Family Violence

1050 Connecticut Avenue, NW
Washington, DC 20036
(202) 429-6695

6033 West Century Boulevard
Los Angeles, CA 90045
(818) 914-2814

A private, national nonprofit organization that provides information about the prevention of all forms of violence within the family and about support services for victims.

■ National Resource Center for Family-Based Services

School of Social Work
University of Iowa
Oakdale, IA 52242
(319) 335-4123

A clearinghouse for information and referrals on family counseling resources around the country.

▲ Parents Without Partners (PWP)/ International Youth Council (IYC)

8807 Colesville Road
Silver Spring, MD 20910
(301) 588-9354

A nonprofit support, educational, and advocacy organization founded in 1957 to promote the welfare and interests of single parents (divorced, widowed, or never married) and their children. In some 1,000 community-based chapters, single parents, their friends, and their children gather to talk about their lives, learn about improving family life, and socialize and play. The **International Youth Council (IYC)** is the young people's branch of PWP. Although IYC doesn't have a large number of chapters, PWP groups themselves offer many activities and services for teens. PWP also produces and distributes a wide variety of publications for and about single-parent families and maintains an information clearinghouse. Information and materials from the headquarters are free or nearly so; local chapters charge small annual dues for membership.

Parents Without Partners has local chapters nationwide and in Canada. In addition to contacting the national office, you can find local chapters listed in the white pages of your phone book under "Parents Without Partners."

▲ Stepfamily Association of America, Inc.

602 East Joppa Road
Baltimore, MD 21204
(301) 823-7570

A national nonprofit educational and support organization whose goal is to improve the chances of success for stepfamilies—families made up of remarried parents and their children. It sponsors local and national gatherings for stepfamily members, produces and distributes informational material, and maintains an educational resources clearinghouse. There is a small membership fee, but you can receive information at little or no cost.

Stepfamily Association of America has local chapters in most parts of the country. In addition to contacting the national office, you can find local chapters listed in the white pages of your phone book under "Stepfamily Association of America, Inc."

▲ THEOS

1301 Clark Building
717 Liberty Avenue
Pittsburgh, PA 15222
(412) 471-7779

A self-help group whose initials stand for "They Help Each Other Spiritually." It was formed for and by young and middle-aged widows and widowers and their families as a way of finding support in the rebuilding of their lives following the premature death of a spouse or parent.

THEOS has local chapters nationwide. In addition to contacting the national office, you can find local chapters listed in the white pages of your phone book under "THEOS."

CONNECT

Remember: When you connect by phone, you can get help without revealing your identity, if you like.

When you connect by mail, you must *give your name and address (including ZIP code) in order to receive help—and a large SASE will speed the response.*

When you contact a group that can help you through a family crisis, you can say:

"I am ____________ years old. I live in ______________, and there's this problem in my family: ______________. What can I do about it?"

If it's hard to be that specific, you can say:

"Please send me information about ______________." or,

"If there's this problem— ______________ —in a family, what can your organization do to help?"

The more information you feel comfortable giving, the more useful will be the help you receive.

Keep in mind that you're looking for help for *yourself* and that your best help will be something that's free and close at hand.

If you ask for information and are concerned about someone else in the family seeing it, you can check to be sure that the material will come without the group's name on the envelope.

GET HELP

You are likely to find that the first help you get from contacting these groups may come from the simple act of asking. Communicating with someone else about your trouble at home can, by itself, make you feel much better. And then, when you find that there are others who are living through family crises like yours, you'll feel better still.

But you'll get more concrete help, as well. When you connect with a self-help group like Al-Anon, Gam-Anon, or Families Anonymous, your request, by phone or mail, will be answered by a member of the group who personally understands your situation and who will provide locations of nearby meetings or a local number to call for information. When you phone locally, your call will also be answered by someone who has shared experiences similar to yours. If you attend a meeting, you will find a group of the same kind of people, talking out troubles that are similar to yours and giving each other support. You won't be asked to give your name, sign anything, or pay anything. When you attend the meeting or read the material, you won't learn how to "cure" or fight the troubled family member; in fact, you'll learn that you can't do that. Rather, you'll discover how to make the most of yourself and *your* life.

Support groups like Parents Without Partners or the Stepfamily Association will refer you to local chapters that sponsor get-togethers where you and your parent will find people who have the same kinds of problems and pleasures as you do. There you will discover how to turn what may seem a liability into an advantage.

Resource and referral agencies can provide information on your family problem and can tell you where, within your community, you can find counseling, support, or other help.

MORE HELP

Within your own community you can find a wide variety of public and private services to help you and your family with all sorts of family crises at little or no cost.

For instance, if addiction is a problem in your family, you may be able to find a **Nar-Anon** group, which provides services for addicts' families similar to those that Al-Anon provides for families of alcoholics. Check the phone book or contact Narcotics Anonymous (see page 24). Also, increasing numbers of hospital drug-treatment centers around the country are initiating special service programs, called COSA, for "children of substance abusers." If you are in that category, call the hospitals in your area to see if their drug-abuse programs have or can refer you to such a program.

If you live in a single-parent family or one with difficulties, find out if there are **Big Brothers/Big Sisters** volunteers in your area who can help you focus on enjoying your *own* life.

In short, almost *any* kind of disorder or disease can create dis-order and dis-ease in a family: the critical illness, death, disability, mental illness, or unemployment of a family member can create a crisis (reread the list on page 4). Just as you'd get a doctor's advice for any persistent pain or fever, so it's important to get as much help and support as you can when home life is a problem.

For support and guidance through any sort of family crisis, you can turn to the clergy, a teacher, a coach, or any trusted adult for support. Or you can find counseling at the **Salvation Army** or the **Volunteers of America** chapters in your community. See the phone book. For information about other local resources, call the local **Red Cross** chapter, the social services office of your **local hospital,** and public or private **community service and social welfare agencies.**

Even though by phoning, you can maintain your anonymity and your family's privacy, be prepared to detail your family situation as much as you can. And remember that these agencies are there to help *you*—so try to let them.

See also: Depending on the specific problem in your family, you may find help from the resources listed in sections in this book on "Abuse" (pages 13–21), "Addiction and Alcoholism" (pages 22–29), "Legal Matters" (pages 70–75), "Mental Health and Suicide" (pages 76–82), or "Running Away" (pages 83–86).

HEALTH CARE

"Adolescent medicine" is a specialty within the medical profession, and with good reason: as complicated socially and emotionally as the teen years can be, they are even more complex physically, since the body undergoes growth and changes more radical than at any other time. So even if you are very healthy and have never had a serious medical problem, you still need competent medical care. A doctor should check out your "new" body, to make sure all systems are functioning smoothly.

When you are not feeling well, it's important to have a doctor check your condition before something more serious develops. And it's comforting, when you're sick, to have a doctor who thoroughly knows about *your* kind of body.

If you ever need hospitalization or other major medical treatment, you'll feel more secure having someone there who knows your special needs—and in any case, you'll benefit from having a professional who can explain your newly developed systems and answer all those questions you may feel timid about asking.

Even if your health is good, you may want a specialist of some kind: a gynecologist for girls, for instance, or a sports medicine expert for athletes. But what is especially valuable right now is a doctor experienced with this physiological stage and trained to understand how the "physical" fits into the "social" and "emotional." (If you have an ongoing health problem, see the suggestions under "Disabilities" on pages 35–41.)

In this section, you'll learn how to find an adolescent specialist as well as sources for other medical information.

To solve the problems in your life that are related to Health Care:

CONTACT

▲ *Sources marked with this symbol will provide direct help for your problem.*

■ *Sources marked with this symbol will provide information and/or referral that will help with your problem.*

▲ Children's Hospice International

1101 King Street
Alexandria, VA 22314
(703) 684-0330

A professional group that provides information and support for seriously ill young people and their families.

■ National Center for Youth Law/Adolescent Health Care Project

1663 Mission Street
San Francisco, CA 94103
(415) 543-3307

A center that can direct you to sources for health care.

■ National Health Information Clearinghouse

P.O. Box 1133
Washington, DC 20013
(301) 565-4167 or 1-800-336-4797

A government resource that can answer any health question or refer you to a source for help and information.

▲ Self-Help Clearinghouse

St. Claires–Riverside Medical Center
Denville, NJ 07834
(201) 625-7101

The place to contact if you need information or support to deal with a specific disease or disorder—even a very rare one. The Self-Help Clearinghouse maintains an extensive list of self-help groups whose members can share their firsthand experience with a huge variety of physical problems and medical situations.

▲ Society for Adolescent Medicine

10727 White Oak Avenue
Suite 101
Granada Hills, CA 91344
(818) 368-5996

Your first contact for a doctor in your area who specializes in caring for adolescents. If you send the society a stamped, self-addressed envelope, you will receive a list of adolescent clinics, physicians, and other health care professionals in your area. If you have a specific question, the society may be able to answer it directly or refer you to someone who can.

CONNECT

Remember: When you connect by phone, you can get help without revealing your identity, if you like.

When you connect by mail, you must *give your name and address (including ZIP code) in order to receive help—and a large SASE will speed the response.*

Depending on your situation, you can say, simply:

"I am ______________ years old, I live in ______________, and I am looking for a doctor." or, add some details:

"I am looking for a doctor because I think I have this medical problem: ______________."

Medical treatment is one area where your youth may get in the way in some cases, so ask these questions first:

"How much does it cost?"

"Is treatment confidential?"

"Do I need parental permission?"

If you are seeking help or information about a specific health problem, be as specific as you can with your question: "What are the symptoms of syphilis?" will get you more useful information than "What causes a rash?"

If the agency you contact does not have the help you seek, ask for suggestions of other places to call.

GET HELP

When you receive the information you requested, your next step will likely be a visit to a doctor or clinic. To get help there, you'll need to be as open and honest as you can about your concerns. An adolescent specialist, though, should be familiar enough with people your age to help you ask the right questions.

If you find, as you may, that you have more than one health professional to choose from, consider these factors when deciding whom to rely on for your health care:

- Who is most responsive to your questions and concerns?
- Whose hours and locations are most convenient?
- Who charges least?

See Chapter Three, "What to Ask," for more suggestions, and remember: it's *your* body. You need to understand it thoroughly and have help in caring for it—so be sure to ask *all* your questions, and find someone who will answer them.

If you do have a health problem, the help you get will consist of the proper treatment for it. And even if you find that you are perfectly healthy, that's a big help, too. It's one less thing on your mind.

MORE HELP

You probably have more adolescent health resources in your own community than you may realize. For example, call your local **hospitals** to see if they have "adolescent clinics" or "adolescent units" that serve teens. Many **high schools** have thorough health-care facilities; see what your school system offers. Also, your school nurse or the physician whom your school has on call probably knows the nearby doctors who treat adolescents. Many **community youth centers** and **Red Cross** chapters offer some form of health care—or they can refer you to it.

See also: To find care for some of the most common, and often most serious, health problems, see such specific resources as those listed under: "Addiction and Alcoholism" (pages 22–29), "Disabilities" (pages 35–41), "Mental Health and Suicide" (pages 76–82), and "Sexual Health" (pages 87–94).

LEGAL MATTERS

Many people mistakenly assume that if you're not an adult, you have no rights. This is no more true than the idea that young people can't get into *real* trouble with the law.

The facts are that you have well-defined legal rights, privileges, and responsibilities in relation to your family, your school, commerce, the government, and society as a whole—and if you commit a crime, you can be punished. But you are *also* entitled to legal counsel. Some of these issues are detailed further on pages 111–114, "You *Do* Have Rights."

The tricky part is that, depending on the situation, your legal status may vary from state to state. So if you think you're being treated unfairly, or if you're considering an undertaking that you have questions about, you'll be wise to talk with a legal professional.

You would also be wrong if you assumed that all legal advice is expensive. In fact, at little or no cost, the resources listed here can provide you with detailed information, advice, and counsel for a specific legal question or problem.

To solve the problems in your life that are related to Legal Matters:

CONTACT

▲ *Sources marked with this symbol will provide direct help for your problem.*

■ *Sources marked with this symbol will provide information and/or referral that will help with your problem.*

▲ The American Civil Liberties Union (ACLU)

132 West 43d Street
New York, NY 10036
(212) 944-9800

A national, nonprofit organization dedicated to the protection of Americans' civil rights as they are defined in the U.S. Constitution and Bill of Rights. The ACLU and its regional offices provide free information and referrals for those with legal concerns related to their civil rights, and, depending on the circumstances, they provide legal counsel and defense. One area of special ACLU interest and expertise is juvenile justice. They produce and distribute an excellent handbook, *The Rights of Young People*, which is available from the headquarters office and in many bookstores at a cost of about $5.00.

The American Civil Liberties Union has local offices in every state and many localities. In addition to contacting the national headquarters, you can find local offices listed in the white pages of your phone book under "ACLU" or your state or city name (for example, "Wisconsin Civil Liberties Union" or "Chicago Civil Liberties Union").

■ Coalition for Juvenile Justice

1400 I Street, NW
Washington, DC 20005
(202) 682-4114

A private group that can provide information on legal issues concerning young people.

▲ Legal Aid Society

National Legal Aid and Defender Association
1625 K Street, NW
Washington, DC 20006
(202) 452-0620

Legal Aid lawyers will provide you with legal advice and representation if you cannot afford to pay lawyers' fees.

Most communities have agencies that provide free legal services. Many but not all of these agencies go by the name "Legal Aid Society," so you can look that up in the white pages of your phone book. Or see "Legal Aid" or "Legal Services" in the yellow pages. If you don't find what you need, ask the National Legal Aid and Defender Association.

■ National Association of Counsel for Children

1205 Oneida Street
Denver, CO 80220
(303) 321-3963

A network of professionals concerned with the legal protection of young people. It provides information on juvenile law.

■ National Center for Youth Law

1663 Mission Street
San Francisco, CA 94103
(415) 543-3307

Experts in juvenile law who provide assistance and information to lawyers on cases involving young people.

■ National Criminal Justice Reference Service

U.S. Department of Justice
P.O. Box 6000
Rockville, MD 10850
1-800-638-8736

A government program that provides information and referrals on legal matters that involve crime.

CONNECT

Remember: When you connect by phone, you can get help without revealing your identity, if you like.

When you connect by mail, you must *give your name and address (including ZIP code) in order to receive help—and a large SASE will speed the response.*

If you find yourself in a situation where you need legal help—or if you even *think* you are being treated unfairly or illegally—you can get information from the groups listed here simply by saying:

"I am ______________ years old, and I have this legal problem [or question]. What can you do to help me?"

When you contact any of the groups, the person on the phone will need to know your age, where you live, the details of your problem, and what kind of help you're seeking. *You* will want to know how much, if anything, the service will cost; whether it is confidential; and whether you need parental permission to get help. If one group can't help, ask for suggestions of others.

GET HELP

When you connect with a legal information service, you will be told or sent the answer to your question free, or you'll be referred to a local or special legal resource that can help you at little or no cost.

If you do need to take the next step and talk with a lawyer, remember that:

- You'll need to be as honest and thorough as you can be in your conversation. *You* will have to provide help in getting legal help.
- The lawyer is working for *you*, so it's your goals and wishes that count.
- You *do* have rights (see pages 111–114). And beware of lawyers in *private* practice who advertise "free legal advice." There's a lot of "fine print" in those promises, so take care.

MORE HELP

You can also get information and advice from your state or local **bar association** (lawyers' professional organization) and by calling the **juvenile or family court** in your city or county. Many **law schools** operate legal clinics or community law projects—check them out, too. Remember that the telephone protects your identity while giving you access to information.

See also: Many of the groups listed in other sections will act as or find legal advocates for their clients. So look under specific categories, like "Abuse" (pages 13–21) or "Disabilities" (pages 35–41), for instance. And for general information about your legal rights and responsibilities, see pages 111–114.

MENTAL HEALTH AND SUICIDE

You needn't be "crazy" to seek help from a mental health professional. In fact, it's often the sanest thing you can do. Simply being an adolescent can make someone *feel* crazy, with all its new physical changes and sensations and with the mood swings often caused by surges of new hormones. Add to that the pressures most teens experience from school, family, and peers, and it's natural that even a young person with no major problems might need a little help in sorting out life.

Often, too, difficulties considered "normal" in today's world create hidden stresses that result in the kinds of symptoms listed on pages 4–5. Professional help can relieve those discomforts.

On a more serious level: depression. Long-term depression, in mild or severe forms, affects teenagers more than any other kind of mental or emotional distress (and it is often made worse by the use of alcohol or other drugs). Everyone gets sad or down sometimes, but for many young people, the symptoms persist. Those symptoms include insomnia, chronic fatigue, drug abuse, outbursts of rage, and feelings of deep sadness. And it can lead to the ultimate, and most tragic, symptom: suicide. Suicide is the third most common form of death among young people. It's final—and it doesn't have to happen.

One good way of heading off such serious trouble is to get help as soon as the trouble is triggered. Family crises and other traumas, for instance, are often hard for anyone to deal with. So in times like those it only makes sense to get help.

The organizations listed here make it simple, and in most cases are free.

IN AN EMERGENCY—when you or someone close to you seems in danger of self-destruction or harming others, call your local emergency number (Operator or 911) or the suicide emergency number listed at the front of your phone book.

To solve the problems in your life that are related to Mental Health:

CONTACT

▲ *Sources marked with this symbol will provide direct help for your problem.*

■ *Sources marked with this symbol will provide information and/or referral that will help with your problem.*

▲ Adolescent Suicide Hotline

Hotline: 1-800-621-4000

A toll-free national hotline, operated 24 hours a day by Youth Crisis Counseling, where you can call to talk over your problems, whether you feel in imminent danger of suicide or not. Trained volunteers will listen, offer support, and guide you toward ways of resolving the difficulty that is getting you down.

■ American Academy of Child & Adolescent Psychiatry

3615 Wisconsin Avenue, NW
Washington, DC 20016
(202) 966-7300

A professional association that provides information about problems and treatments common among young people.

■ American Society for Adolescent Psychiatry

5530 Wisconsin Avenue
Washington, DC 20815
(301) 652-0646

A national association of psychiatrists that can provide names of professionals in your area who specialize in treating adolescents.

■ Center for Adolescent Mental Health

Columbia University School of Social Work
622 West 113th Street
New York, NY 10025
(212) 280-4088

A research group that provides information about adolescent mental health and about programs that promote it.

▲ Emotions Anonymous/Youth Emotions Anonymous

P.O. Box 4245
St. Paul, MN 55104
(612) 647-9712

A nonprofit, nonsectarian self-help fellowship of people who meet regularly to share support and experience toward developing healthy emotions and attitudes while finding resolutions to the problems in their lives. Based on the principles and techniques of Alcoholics Anonymous (see page 23), but not affiliated with it, EA is not professional therapy. Rather, members find help through a network of support. **Youth Emotions Anonymous** is a program for those aged 13 through 19, led by practicing adult members of EA. There are no dues, fees, or costs, and no membership requirements.

Emotions Anonymous has local chapters nationwide and internationally. In addition to contacting the national office, you can find local chapters listed in the white pages of your phone book under "Emotions Anonymous."

■ National Institute of Mental Health

5600 Fishers Lane
Rockville, MD 20857
(301) 443-4513

A government agency that offers a free directory of community mental health centers as well as other information about mental health.

■ Youth Suicide National Center

445 Virginia Avenue
San Mateo, CA 94402
(415) 342-5755

A research group and clearinghouse that provides information about suicide prevention and offers referrals to support groups for those who have considered suicide.

CONNECT

Remember: When you connect by phone, you can get help without revealing your identity, if you like.

When you connect by mail, you must *give your name and address (including ZIP code) in order to receive help—and a large SASE will speed the response.*

This is an area where it can be particularly hard to express what you want or need, so you can say something as simple as:

"I am ______________ years old, and I have troubles I can't seem to get off my mind. What can your group do for me?" or,

"I have a friend who is thinking about suicide." or,

"Can you help me?"

The person with whom you connect has the training or experience to help you tell as much of your story as possible.

Often, it's the connecting itself that's important.

GET HELP

As in other kinds of situations, the first help you'll receive from contacting these organizations is the feeling of relief you'll experience just from sharing your worries with someone else: it opens the door to more valuable help.

When you call a suicide hotline, you'll get a good listener who can suggest ways to deal with your immediate feelings and to get help for your broader problems.

A call to Emotions Anonymous will get you some informational pamphlets if you choose to give your name and address. Whether you give your name or not, you will be told how to contact a group in your area. If you attend a meeting, you will find others like yourself talking about the troubles, feelings, and worries that they suffered with—and often almost died from—and how they have found ways to work them out positively with the help of others in the program.

The information and referral services will answer your questions and direct you to agencies near your home that can provide further help.

If you decide to visit a therapist or a mental health clinic, you can receive ongoing professional guidance. (For suggestions on how best to deal with professional therapists, see the section on "Health Care."

MORE HELP

You can also find free or low-cost mental health guidance in your community through the adolescent unit of your local **hospital**; the state, county, or city **office of child welfare or youth services;** and the **community mental health center**. Check your phone book for addresses and telephone numbers.

See also: Because other problems can be the cause or the result of mental illness, you may also find help from resources listed under "Abuse" (pages 13–21), "Addiction and Alcoholism" (pages 22–29), "Family Crises" (pages 55–64), or "Health Care" (pages 65–69).

RUNNING AWAY

Running away from home is one of the most drastic steps, short of suicide, that a young person can take, because no matter how bad things may seem at home, things are likely to be worse "out there." That's why so many organizations, like those listed here, exist to help runaways and their families. They are all easy to reach and ready to act, whether you are a runaway, are considering leaving home, or know someone who is.

One good way to avoid having to face the problems that runaways encounter, of course, is to get help in solving the problems you may think you're running away from. Many young people leave home to escape abuse or other family crises or trouble with the law or in school. So in addition to following the suggestions in this section, see if you can't find the help you need from some of the groups listed in any of the other sections of this book.

Some young people don't run away voluntarily: thousands of children and teens are classified as "missing," most often taken from home by a parent or other relative in a family dispute. If you are among those and you want to go home, you'll find help here, too.

Often it is not only the runaway who needs help. The families and friends who are left behind when someone disappears need help, as well, and the groups listed in this section can provide it.

To solve the problems in your life that are related to Running Away:

CONTACT

▲ *Sources marked with this symbol will provide direct help for your problem.*

■ *Sources marked with this symbol will provide information and/or referral that will help with your problem.*

▲ Child Find, Inc.

P.O. Box 277
New Paltz, NY 12561
Hotline: 1-800-I-AM-LOST

A toll-free hotline through which missing children and young people can find their way home and families of the missing can find support. The group also maintains an information and communications network devoted to finding missing children.

▲ National Runaway Switchboard

Hotline: 1-800-621-4000

A hotline operated 24 hours a day by trained volunteers who can talk with runaways about their problems, refer them to needed services, or advise the families of runaways about available help.

▲ The Nine-Line

Hotline: 1-800-999-9999

A 24-hour-a-day helpline for runaways and abandoned children, operated by Covenant House, a teen shelter in New York City.

For those who are considering running away and their families, trained operators give help, support, advice, and referrals to social-service agencies.

■ Runaway Hotline

Hotline: 1-800-231-6946 [Texas: 1-800-392-3352]

A toll-free hotline that will tell runaways where to find services and shelters, wherever they are having trouble.

■ U.S. Department of Health and Human Services

Family and Youth Services Bureau
P.O. Box 1182
Washington, DC 20013
(202) 755-7800

The federal government's **Runaway and Homeless Youth Program** can provide information on the nearly 350 shelters around the country that offer not only temporary housing but health care, educational and job training programs, and legal aid.

CONNECT

Remember: When you connect by phone, you can get help without revealing your identity, if you like.

When you connect by mail, you must *give your name and address (including ZIP code) in order to receive help—and a large SASE will speed the response.*

When you call these services, you needn't give your name; just describe your situation. For example:

"I am ________________ years old, away from home, and I don't know where to go." or,

"My sister ran away from home, and the whole family's going nuts." or,

"I have a friend who's thinking of running away."

You are best off, of course, if you call *before* you leave home. So think about what it is you're thinking of running away *from*—abuse, neglect, family fights—and try to talk about that.

GET HELP

The free services listed here can help you (and your family) if you are a runaway, if you are thinking of running away, if you have been separated from home against your will, or if someone else in your family has run away or disappeared. They will direct the runaway to vital services and offer advice and support, they will help families trace children, and they will contact the runaway's family if (*and only if*) asked to.

MORE HELP

If you are a runaway seeking shelter, or if you are trying to find someone who has run away, you should know that every state and most large cities offer runaway services and the **Red Cross** and **Salvation Army** are always good places to turn.

See also: The best help comes *before* running away, so contact the groups listed in these sections *first*: "Abuse" (pages 13–21), "Addiction and Alcoholism" (pages 22–29), "Family Crises" (pages 55–64), or "Mental Health and Suicide" (pages 76–82).

SEXUAL HEALTH

Whether it's AIDS, birth control, pregnancy, sexual identity, or just how to say "no," more young people have more questions and concerns about this most personal area of their lives than about any other topic—yet it's here that the questions may be the hardest to ask, and the answers, many believe, are the hardest to find.

Even basic facts about how your body works may be puzzling to you, as it is for many people of all ages. Your body itself, with all its changes and new sensations, brings enough confusion. Then our society adds to that confusion, because nature develops adult bodies long before the world in which we must live says we're adults.

The people who provide information and advice through the organizations listed here understand that. Not only do they have the facts you need right now, but they can explain them in a way that's comfortable for you. And you can often get this kind of very personal information for free and without revealing much or anything about yourself.

"Sexual health" means more than knowledgeable care of one's reproductive system; it means healthy attitudes and behavior and the sense of feeling comfortable with one's self.

To solve the problems in your life that are related to Sexual Health:

CONTACT

▲ *Sources marked with this symbol will provide direct help for your problem.*

■ *Sources marked with this symbol will provide information and/or referral that will help with your problem.*

▲ Association of Junior Leagues, Inc.

660 First Avenue
New York, NY 10016
(212) 683-1515

This voluntary organization operates the **Teen Outreach Program (TOP)**, which provides special weekly programs whose goal is to reduce teenage pregnancy and thereby help young people complete high school.

The Junior League has local chapters nationwide. In addition to contacting the national office, you can find local chapters (and/or receive information about TOP activities) listed in the white pages of your phone book under "Junior League."

■ Center for Population Options

1012 14th Street, NW
Washington, DC 20005
(202) 347-5700

A private nonprofit group whose goal is to help teens make sensible decisions about the course of their lives through combining family planning and sexual health with life-planning skills. It can provide information about local programs.

■ Family Life Information Exchange

P.O. Box 10716
Rockville, MD 20850
(301) 770-3662

An agency that provides information on family planning issues.

▲ Institute for the Protection of Lesbian and Gay Youth

401 West Street
New York, NY 10014
(212) 633-8920
(212) 473-4197 for the hearing-impaired

This association of professionals promotes the mental and physical well-being of homosexual young people through free and confidential counseling, education, and referral services. Although its activities are located primarily in the New York area, it can provide information and serve as a resource for similar services elsewhere.

■ March of Dimes

1725 K Street, NW
Washington, DC 20006
(202) 659-1800

A national nonprofit organization whose purpose is the prevention of birth defects. Pregnant teens can receive information in order to get the special help required to assure a healthy pregnancy.

The March of Dimes has local chapters nationwide. In addition to contacting the national office, you can find chapters listed in the white pages of your phone book under "March of Dimes."

■ National AIDS Network

2033 M Street, NW
Washington, DC 20036
(202) 293-2437

A national central clearinghouse for information on Acquired Immune Deficiency Syndrome (AIDS), which can provide information on the disease and on local organizations that provide help.

■ National Clearinghouse for Health Information

1010 Wayne Avenue
Silver Spring, MD 20910
(202) 565-4167 or 1-800-336-4797

A federal government service providing free information on all diseases, including the sexually transmitted ones: AIDS, herpes, syphilis, gonorrhea, chlamydia, and others.

■ National Organization on Adolescent Pregnancy and Parenting

P.O. Box 2365
Reston, VA 22090
(703) 435-3948

A clearinghouse for information to help teenage parents and for referral to local service agencies.

▲ National Right to Life Committee

419 7th Street, NW
Washington, DC 20004
(202) 626-8800

A national nonprofit organization with a primary focus on the protection of the unborn. Its **National Teens Life** groups offer pregnant teens free information, counseling and referral to services that provide alternatives to abortion. No age restrictions.

National Right to Life Committee has local chapters nationwide. In addition to contacting the national office, you can find local chapters listed in the white pages of your phone book under "National Right to Life Committee."

▲ Planned Parenthood Federation of America, Inc.

810 Seventh Avenue
New York, NY 10019
(212) 541-7800

A national nonprofit medical and educational organization that provides help, information, and counseling on all aspects of sexuality and reproductive health. All services are readily available to adolescents, and free unless you can afford a small fee. (*Note*: In some states parental consent is required for abortions.) One-on-one counseling is an integral part of its services to young people.

Planned Parenthood has nearly 200 centers nationwide. In addition to contacting the national office, you can find local centers listed in the white pages of your phone book under "Planned Parenthood" or in the yellow pages under "Family Planning" or "Social Service Agencies."

■ **Sex Information and Education Council of the U.S.**
32 Washington Place
New York, NY 10003
(212) 673-3850
A clearinghouse that provides information on every aspect of sexuality.

CONNECT

Remember: When you connect by phone, you can get help without revealing your identity, if you like.

When you connect by mail, you must *give your name and address (including ZIP code) in order to receive help—and a large SASE will speed the response.*

"I think I may be pregnant, and I don't want to have an abortion. Where can I get help?" or,

"I am ______________ years old and I am [pregnant, in need of birth control, worried about disease, confused about sex . . .]. Where can I get help?"

These are the kinds of questions that young people ask the helping organizations listed here. Also:

"How does someone know if he's gay?" or,

"Can you get AIDS from kissing?"

You can call these numbers and ask any question you want about anything that's on your mind concerning sex, pregnancy, or sexual health. That's what they're there for (and if you're concerned about confidentiality, ask).

If you feel uncomfortable making a phone call like that, even though the telephone allows you to remain anonymous, you can call or write, asking,

"Please send me information about [AIDS, pregnancy . . .] or,

"Please send me information about your organization."

Sometimes, people feel foolish or embarrassed asking questions about sex, but just keep in mind that you'll feel much more than "foolish" if you have to live with the consequences of actions you've taken based on *mis*information.

GET HELP

These organizations will give you exactly the help you *want*. Depending on where you live, there may be some limitations because of your age, but most centers are able to fill *your* needs, and in confidence.

At a National Teens Life center and at other places like it, for instance, you will receive information about where to get free medical help during pregnancy and where to go for counseling on every aspect of pregnancy—from temporary housing through placing a baby for adoption or support in parenting skills.

At a Planned Parenthood center or similar clinic, counselors and health care professionals answer your questions; give you medical exams and tests; provide contraceptives and birth control information; prescribe other needed medication and treatment; perform an abortion if you want or provide prenatal care; and refer you to other services within the community as needed. Services are free, or based on ability to pay, and all are confidential. You can also find out about individual, group, or family counseling programs and information workshops where you can learn about and discuss sexuality, parenting, sexual abuse, and sex-related diseases, including AIDS.

From the more specialized centers, you'll get information or referrals that will guide you in managing this complex, and often frightening, area of life.

Since there is such a wide variety of resources available, you need only accept the help and advice that's right for you. *No one can force you to take an action that seems inappropriate.* (So if you find yourself in a clinic that's applying pressure along with its "help," you can leave.)

MORE HELP

You can also get help and information on sexual health and sexually transmitted diseases by calling or visiting your local **hospital**, **clinic**, or **youth center**.

See also: Entries in the section on "Health Care" (pages 65–69) suggest resources for maintenance of sexual health and for the development of a healthy attitude about your whole body.

WORK AND MONEY

No matter what your age, "work" can mean more than odd jobs, and "money" can mean something other than a weekly allowance or minimum wage. As a teen, you do face stricter limits than if you were older, largely because of laws that were designed to protect young people. That doesn't mean, though, that you should automatically assume you have to wait until you're "grown up" to do grown-up business. You have a right to work, in most states, once you reach age 14, though limitations do apply.

These days, you are likely to find a lot of Help Wanted signs in stores and small businesses around your community because you're living in a labor pool that's growing smaller (see page 104). Working in a stockroom or at a fast-food counter may be convenient to your school schedule, but remember that you don't *have* to settle for a stopgap job. You can find ways to explore a career that you're considering—by volunteering or by applying to work at apprentice-level wages in an organization that interests you.

If you decide to get a job "only for the money," you have, in most cases, the right to earn a minimum wage. By law, your parents are probably entitled to your wages because they are required by law to support *you.* (They must also pay you if you work for a family business.) Even if they don't exert their right to *take* your pay, they'll probably be happier if you use some of it to defray personal, educational, or other expenses rather than just sock it away while you live off their salaries. In fact, most college-scholarship programs require that you make a contribution from your own savings or earnings.

On the other hand, in most states you may open a bank account that is accessible only by you. You can also invest money, within the limits of rules that apply to minors' legal contracts (see "Legal Matters," page 70). And, of course, you have the very grown-up obligation of filing a tax return for every year in which you earn a certain minimum amount of money.

Through various public and private programs, you can get free vocational training, and you'll find youth groups that offer career-related experience. When you're ready for college, you can arrange to combine work with study (see "Education and Scholarships," page 47). In some cases, you can even live on your own as an adult before you reach the age of "majority" (see page 111–113).

However you work it out, working your way toward your goals is one of the best ways to help yourself. So gather as much information and direct help as you can from the resources listed here.

To solve the problems in your life that are related to Work and Money:

CONTACT

▲ *Sources marked with this symbol will provide direct help for your problem.*

■ *Sources marked with this symbol will provide information and/or referral that will help with your problem.*

▲ American ORT Federation

817 Broadway
New York, NY 10003
(212) 677-4400

A private, international group that offers vocational and technical education to Jewish youth.

■ Frontlash

815 16th Street, NW
Washington, DC 20006
(202) 783-3993

An organization promoting collaboration between youth and the labor-union movement, which can provide guidance on finding work.

▲ National Alliance of Business

1015 15th Street, NW
Washington, DC 20005
(202) 457-0040

A private association of employers that develops summer jobs that it offers to disadvantaged youth.

■ National Child Labor Committee

1501 Broadway
New York, NY 10036
(212) 840-1801

A national organization of employers, unions, and youth-work experts that can refer you to information and advice about labor laws, youth-employment programs, co-op education, and other job-related resources.

■ National Collaboration for Youth

1319 F Street, NW
Washington, DC 20004
(202) 347-2080

A national coalition of youth-serving organizations that can refer you to job-training and career-counseling services within your community.

▲ National Youth Employment Coalition

1501 Broadway
New York, NY 10036
(212) 840-1801

A national network of public and private organizations that provide support, information, or training for youth workers. Contact the coalition for referral to a member-agency that meets your needs.

▲ Project 70001 Training and Employment

600 Maryland Avenue, SW
Washington, DC 20024
(202) 484-0103

A network of state programs that offer high school dropouts training and employment.

■ U.S. Department of Labor

Employment and Training Administration
200 Constitution Avenue, NW
Washington, DC 20210
(202) 523-6871

The government agency that administers all federal job training programs and that can provide information about work-related projects that can be useful to you.

The U.S. Department of Labor has regional offices nationwide. In addition to contacting the national office, you can find regional offices listed in the "U.S. Government" section of your phone book.

Your state department of labor can connect you with jobs or training programs that it sponsors.

CONNECT

Remember: *When you connect by phone, you can get help without revealing your identity, if you like.*

When you connect by mail, you must *give your name and address (including ZIP code) in order to receive help—and a large SASE will speed the response.*

Now that you've read through this section, give some thought to the kind of help you want.

- Do you want a job, any job, that will bring in income now?
- Or do you want a training program that will lead to a better job later?
- Are you eligible for special government-sponsored programs?
- Do you want work, even for low pay, that will give you experience?
- Do you want help in finding answers to these questions?

Then, pick the organization that seems most likely to help you find the right work for you, and get in touch with them.

GET HELP

Some of the organizations you connect with will be able to provide you with work or training directly. Others will give you general information about employment and job hunting as well as listings of groups within your area that offer more specific work-related help.

Finding the right work, at any age, can often mean making a lot of phone calls, so if the first connection doesn't get you the help you need, ask for suggestions about where else to phone.

MORE HELP

You can also find free training and/or job placement through **community centers** in your neighborhood; through your **state's employment service**; and through special **youth employment projects** that your city or county may offer. Also, look into **work-study or co-op education projects** in high schools or colleges.

In addition, you can gain training and experience toward the career of your choice, as well as general job-seeking and job-holding skills, through participation in any of the following groups. All have local chapters, so check the white pages of your phone book.

Future Business Leaders of America
1901 Association Drive
Reston, VA 22091
(703) 860-3334

Future Farmers of America
5632 Mt. Vernon Memorial Highway
Alexandria, VA 22309
(703) 360-3600

Future Homemakers of America
1910 Association Drive
Reston, VA 22091
(703) 476-4900

Junior Achievement, Inc.
45 Clubhouse Drive
Colorado Springs, CO 80906
(303) 540-8000

National 4-H Council
7100 Connecticut Avenue
Chevy Chase, MD 20815
(301) 961-2800

Vocational Industrial Clubs of America
P.O. Box 3000
Leesburg, VA 22075
(703) 777-8810

You'll also gain career skills and experience through participation in special programs of **social-service organizations** like the Red Cross, Scouts, Camp Fire, Boys Clubs, Girls Clubs, and YMCA and YWCA. Check out your local groups to see what they offer.

Whereas the organizations listed here may be able to help you with contacts or placement, you can also do it on your own by looking in the **want ads** of your local paper, by checking **community bulletin boards**, or by using your phone book's **yellow pages** to locate organizations or businesses that appeal to you and applying for work there.

Don't forget that the **military** is a leading employer of young people, once you are old enough to enlist (that has disadvantages, of course, but many benefits as well). And when you are somewhat older, there's **VISTA** and the **Peace Corps**.

Whatever you decide on, don't take on more than you can handle. Success in school is more important to your long-term success than paid work today. Still, don't sell yourself short as an earner.

CHAPTER THREE

WHAT TO ASK

As you can see from the preceding chapters, whatever your problem may be, you don't have to face it alone.

But wherever you turn for support and guidance, you can't expect them to do it all—you need to help them help you. This chapter will show you, in detail, how to get the most from the help that is available.

WHAT'S AVAILABLE

First, let's look at *availability*. Although the listings in this book are as thorough and accurate as they could be at the time they were written, they may not be available by the time you read about it here. But as you'll see in this section, other resources *are* available. Here's why.

Just as social and economic changes have made it necessary for young people to look outside their families and their neighborhoods for help with crises, so do they affect the availability of helping resources. Help requires funds from somewhere, especially if that help is free or low in cost to you. The funding of service programs, whether from public or private purses, is often dependent on the politics and popular moods of the time. So when you seek help you may discover people or organizations willing to assist with your particular problem, but unable to do as much as they might like. It's impossible to predict in what social direction money will be flowing by the time you read this book. In the late 1980s, for instance, the federal government declared a "war on drugs," but cut the level of public funding for drug-rehabilitation programs. So if you should ever feel frustrated when seeking help, try not to take it personally, and remember that your helpers are doing the best they can.

On the other side of the coin, people who become teenagers during the 1990s and into the 2000s are likely to find a lot more opportunities available to them. Because of a history of social changes that began four decades earlier, the late 1980s marked the beginning of an era of very small younger generations within the United States population. So you may discover that schools, training programs, and employers are *eager* to see you and that service programs have no waiting lists for their younger clients. The cloud around that silver lining is that funding and public interest may be more focused on services for older Americans.

The point is, society changes, so if you need help, you may need to work within those changes to find it. The good news is, it's *always* available—you just need to know where to look.

Here are some ways and places to look for help of any sort which is not listed in this book.

- Your **library.** Librarians may be able to help you directly with guidance about where to turn in your community, and they will be able to help you use the best directories and files to find the resources you need. Most of the books listed in the "Reading Matter" section of this book (see page 121) are likely to be in the reference section of the library. You can keep your research absolutely private by looking in the library's catalog under the name of the topic that concerns you. Check under the heading "Youth," as well—and if you're unsure of how to use the catalog, ask the librarian. Also, many larger libraries have special service centers specifically for young people or for information and assistance related to education and employment.

- Your **phone book.** The white pages list organizations by name in alphabetical order. Find "Alcoholics Anonymous" in the "A's," for instance, or see the "Y's" for something like "Youth, County Center for . . ." Look in the yellow pages for categories: "Social Service Organizations" will include a wide range of resources, for example; or see "Colleges," "Counseling," "Youth," and the like. Also, many phone books have a special section—often on blue pages—for government agencies, and the very front of your local directory may list places to phone in a variety of emergencies.
- Depending on your situation, you can also get information and referrals from **hospitals**; **community centers**; **churches** and other religious organizations; or the local **Y**, **Scouts**, **youth center**, or other neighborhood groups.
- Your local **newspaper** is a good resource, too. In the "events," "personals," or "social" sections of many community papers, you'll find where and when various self-help groups meet in your area. And the editorial staff of the paper can also look up information in their files, if you let them know that it's important.
- Starting on **page 115** of this book, you'll find even more suggestions.

So you should realize, by now, that you can always get help. An important question remains: how valuable is it?

WHAT TO ASK

HOW TO RATE THE RESOURCES

Whether you turn up a few or an abundance of resources, you'll need to assure yourself that the help is safe, honest, and right for *you*—and these criteria apply to the organizations listed in this book as well as to those you may gather on your own. None of us wants to take the risk of baring our soul to a stranger without some assurance that the stranger is trustworthy.

Some pointers:

- **Do you get good response?** When you call, is the phone answered courteously? Does the staff seem to have information readily available? Are you asked questions that make sense? If you request information to be mailed, how quickly does it come?
- **Is the help for you?** Does this place offer help for your particular problem? Does it serve people your age? With or without parental permission? Does it offer special guidance for young people? Can you get help at times and places that are convenient for you? (If an organization says it serves teens but requires your presence during school hours or in places where you must be able to drive, it's not too helpful.)
- **Who are the helpers?** Are they trained professionals? Lay people who have had problems similar to yours and are willing to share their experiences? Or are they simply salaried employees with no special training?
- **What's the record?** How long has the service been in operation? How many people has it served? Will it help you find other clients to talk with? If you are left with unanswered questions, check with the Better Business

Bureau, the Chamber of Commerce, or an appropriate professional organization for any previous complaints.

- **What does it cost?** What services does it provide at no or low cost: actual help? information, evaluation, or referral only? If there are costs, how will you be allowed to pay them: all at once? or over time? Will insurance plans or other funds cover the cost?
- **Will they answer your questions?** If you don't receive satisfactory responses to questions like these and others you may have, you may be right in feeling uncomfortable. Try to check further, or find another source. Beware especially a response like, "Once you've paid your fee (or signed on to the program), all your questions will be answered."

Unfortunately, it's true that not all strangers are trustworthy. And there are those individuals and organizations that will take advantage of people—especially young people—who are in the vulnerable position of needing help. So keep in mind these other "Bewares":

- Be suspicious of high costs or of what seem to be hidden fees. Not all services can be free, but a truly helpful organization will keep costs as low—and as open—as possible. Before paying—or agreeing to pay—any fee, be sure that you can't find similar help for free elsewhere.
- Don't believe extravagant promises. Any person or group that says, "We guarantee a cure," "We can solve all your problems," or "You won't have to do a thing—trust me," is probably *not* to be trusted. Nor is any that

requires you to place your faith in the person of any individual. You're not seeking a guru, saint, or "Dr. Cure-all"; you want realistic help to carry through into your daily life.

- If at any point you have doubts or questions about the service or the helper, talk them over with someone else you trust.
- Don't sign any documents! You may be required to register—your name, address, phone number, age, and a bit of other personal information—in order to qualify for some services. But if you're asked to sign your name at the bottom of a page of words, don't do it unless you can get professional, trusted advice first. As a minor (see pages 111–113), you may not be forced to stand by any contract or written promise, but you can sign up for a lot of hassles if you unwittingly agree in writing to anything. Besides, a person or organization that tries to pressure you into signing documents—or into taking *any* other actions they hadn't told you about from the outset—should send you warning signals to go elsewhere.

HOW TO ASK FOR HELP

Those tips and warnings aren't meant to scare you away from getting help, of course, but to ensure that you get the right kind of help. It's important, for many reasons, to remember that even when you ask for help from a source *outside* of yourself, you don't give up helping *yourself*.

You can best help yourself—and your helpers—from the beginning by getting and giving information as clearly and completely as possible. That can be hard, especially when you're nervous or have a lot on your mind. So each "Where to Find Help" section in this book has included a few suggestions on how to connect—of what to say. Here are some more phrases to use when you call or write for help.

Information to Give. Your age, general location, problem, and request: "I am ______________ years old. I live in [neighborhood, town, county, or state]. I think that I may need help with [what?], and I would like to know what you can do for me." Those are the basics that any helper needs in order to know whether you've called the best place. Notice that you don't have to identify yourself if you're asking by phone or in person at a large institution; it's often easier to ask for help if we don't have to reveal our full identities at first.

When writing for information, of course, you'll need to give your name and full address (including ZIP code) to receive material. It's also a good idea to make a note of where and when you wrote so that you can keep tabs on the response.

Information to get. For the basics that *you* need in order to decide where to get help, ask these questions in your letter or conversation or look for the answers in the written material you find or receive about the organization:

- "What kind of help do you provide?"
- "What does it cost?"
- "Is it confidential? What do you need to know about me? What kind of records do you keep and who is allowed to see them?"
- "Can I come on my own, or do I need an adult's permission or referral?"
- "Here's why I think I need help: __________. Do you think I have a problem? Do you think your organization can help me?"
- "What do I do next?"

HOW TO HELP YOUR HELPERS

What to do next, when you've decided to get help, is to do your best to work *with* the service you're offered.

- First, be honest. That's crucial, and it may not be easy. Sometimes, just filling out an application form accurately, as for a scholarship or training program, can be hard: false pride or false modesty can get in the way of the help we need and deserve.

  So it can be even harder when we have to speak with someone. You already know how hard it is to talk about your troubles—even to admit that you need help. But in order to get the help you seek, you have to be as clear and complete as you can when discussing your problems with the people or the groups who can help you solve them. They will make it as easy for you as they can—they have either been there themselves, or they have been trained to understand the kinds of things you face. Nothing that you say will shock or surprise them, because no matter how new the situation is to you, it's not likely to be new to them. And because of their experience, they are likely to know when you're being dishonest or not telling the whole story—so you might as well get it all off your chest.
- Be willing to follow the suggestions you are offered. Sometimes, no matter how much we want help, we've gotten so used to our problems, or so convinced we can't get out of them, that we react negatively to any helpful suggestion: "I can't do that!" "Why bother?

That won't work." "What good will that do?"

Instead, give your helpers the benefit of the doubt and at least try what they suggest. You've got nothing to lose, and since they're the experts, they may know what they're doing.

- Share your own feelings. If at any point you are uncomfortable about anything you're asked about or asked to do, say so, or at least ask for an explanation. A responsible and competent helper will be able to make you feel more comfortable by helping you to understand why this step is needed to achieve your goal.

  And that's what getting help is all about: becoming more comfortable in life or achieving an important goal by turning to some responsible person or group whose experience can increase your own competence.
- Remember, whatever your situation, you are able—and entitled—to get help.

YOU *DO* HAVE RIGHTS: WHAT YOU CAN—AND CAN'T—DO

One basic fact makes it possible for you to get help when you need it: no matter how young you are, you *do* have legal rights. You also have responsibilities under our legal system—and because of your age, the law sets limitations on your rights and responsibilities that are different from those of adults.

It's important to understand your legal rights, responsibilities, and limitations in order to have some idea of what to expect—and what to demand—when you are seeking help.

Each of the fifty states has its own *age of majority*—the age at which a young person becomes an adult. According to the

American Civil Liberties Union, that age is 18 in almost every state. In Alabama, Nebraska, and Wyoming it is 19; in Mississippi and Pennsylvania it is 21. In most—*but not all*—cases, this is the age below which someone is considered a "juvenile" by the criminal justice system.

Details of state laws vary widely. For instance, in many states, although you become a legal adult at 18, you may not be able to purchase alcoholic beverages for one, two, or three more years, while in some places you can buy tobacco—or leave school or get married—at a *younger* age. In many states, too, you can still get certain kinds of medical treatment without parental consent, even though you are still considered a minor. (And there is also a category called "mature minor," which under certain circumstances allows you to get services otherwise reserved for adults.) Rules for the employment of young people vary not only by state, but within counties and municipalities, as well. And your state may have special rules regulating the investment of the money you earn. All these rules may seem complex, but they are written down, and you can find them out from a professional organization. You needn't rely on some amateur's saying, "You can't do that—you're just a kid!"

What can—and can't—you do? *In general*, you, as a young citizen of the United States, are entitled to the same freedoms constitutionally guaranteed to all U.S. citizens. Judgments on these issues change case by case, but generally, you're "entitled" just like everyone else. As a minor, you are also entitled to special protections. These include a right to proper food, health care, shelter, education, and safety, as well as to special treatment by the police and the court system.

Sometimes, because the state has a special interest in your welfare, governmental authorities will step in if your family is not providing for your necessities. This is one reason why young people are sometimes reluctant to seek help no matter how desperate they are—and this is why this book provides phone numbers so that you can call for information about helping resources without revealing your identity. No matter what the rules are in your state, you *can* find help that won't necessarily lead to "more trouble."

Your parents *are* legally allowed to impose rules on you that they couldn't apply to others, and so can the state. As a minor, for instance, there are few contracts and other agreements that you can enter into on your own. And it's unlikely you'll be able to get a credit card or charge account until you are legally an adult since you aren't yet *legally* required to pay your debts. (Your parents, however, are liable for them.) Also, you can be arrested and tried not only for any illegal activity that an adult can but also (depending on the jurisdiction) for such "juvenile" infractions as being a runaway or breaking a curfew.

In *most* "civil matters"—legal controversies that do not involve a crime—minors have special access to a lawyer or other advocate. And if you are accused of any crime, you are entitled to legal help—and the state must provide a lawyer if you can't afford one.

For detailed advice or information about your rights and responsibilities, and about legal questions, you can contact the local office of:

American Civil Liberties Union (ACLU)
132 West 43d Street
New York, NY 10036
(202) 944-9800

You can also read their book, *The Rights of Young People*, or check with the Legal Aid Society (see page 72).

The ACLU can also provide information on the very special status of young people called **legal emancipation**, through which, by the act of a judge, a minor can be partially or completely freed from parental authority.

"Emancipated" status may sound appealing, especially if things seem rough at home or if you're feeling particularly put-upon these days. It's granted only under special circumstances, though, and through careful legal procedures. Also "emancipation," in this case, does not equal "freedom": it's not an escape, any more than running away or getting lost in a drug is an escape. The granting of adult status, even if you are eligible for it, brings with it adult problems.

So if reading about this very specialized form of help for young people sets off bells in your head, don't drop everything and find a lawyer. Instead, you might be better off rereading Chapter One and taking the time to find more specific ways to solve your problems within the other sections of this book. You don't need to be "emancipated" in order to help yourself.

Remember, even though so many of our problems feel so painful and the process of solving them may not seem easy, it will always be simple if you:

CONTACT the best resource.
CONNECT with the best words you can find.
GET HELP to solve the problems in your life.

CHAPTER FOUR

BACKUP

In case you haven't yet found in this book how to get help for your problem, or if you're looking for more information, here's backup material.

HOTLINES AND TOLL-FREE TELEPHONE NUMBERS

These are phone numbers that you can use to call for help or information on a variety of problems.

- In most states, you must dial (or press) "1" before the "800."
- If the 800 number you dial is out of service, if a recorded message tells you that it cannot be reached from your area code, or if you want to phone an organization not listed here, call this number: **1-800-555-1212.** Give the operator your area code and the name of the group.
- If you are deaf or disabled and use special communications devices, call this number if you need help in telephoning: **1-800-855-1155**.

Note: Some of the following groups are described in the "Where to Find Help" sections of this book. Those are marked with a page number to which you can turn for more information.

Some of these numbers are available 24 hours a day, 7 days a week; some only during weekday business hours. All of them offer information and advice at long distance.

But—IF YOU NEED IMMEDIATE HELP IN A DANGEROUS SITUATION, DIAL 911 OR "OPERATOR"!

ABUSE

National Coalition Against Domestic Violence
800-333-7233
(page 16)

National Council on Child Abuse and Family Violence
800-222-2000
(page 17)

Parents Anonymous
800-421-0353
[800-356-0386 in California]
(page 18)

(Also see numbers under Family Crises.)

ADDICTION AND ALCOHOLISM

Cocaine Hotline
800-COCAINE (262-2463)
(page 23)

National Council on **Alcoholism**
800-NCA-CALL (622-2255)
(page 25)

National Federation of Parents for **Drug** Free Youth
800-554-KIDS (554-5437)
[(301) 585-KIDS in Maryland]
(Referrals to support groups and treatment centers)

National Institute on **Drug** Abuse
800-662-HELP (662-4357)
National Parents Resource Institute for **Drug** Education, Inc. (PRIDE)
800-241-7946
(page 26)
(Also see numbers under Family Crises and Health Care.)

DISABILITIES

American Council of the **Blind**
800-424-8666
(Information and referrals to help and advocacy services)
Deafness Research Center
800-835-DEAF (835-3323)
(Information on prevention and treatment of hearing problems)
Higher Education and the Handicapped
800-544-3284
(page 37)
National Center for **Stuttering**
800-221-2483
(Information and advice)
National Organization on **Disability**
800-248-ABLE (248-2253)
[(212) 532-1460 in New York]
(Information on programs to aid the handicapped)
National **Rehabilitation** Information Center
800-34-NARIC (346-2742)
(Information and referral on services for the disabled)
Orton **Dyslexia** Society
800-ABCD-123 (222-3123)

(Referrals to support groups and services)

Recording for the **Blind**, Inc.

800-221-4792

(Free cassettes of books from the Library of Congress)

Self-Help Clearinghouse

800-367-6274

(page 38)

Spinal Cord Injury Neurological Recovery Center

800-526-3456

(Information on aids and services for the disabled)

(Also see numbers under Family Crises and Health Care.)

EDUCATION AND SCHOLARSHIPS

United Student Aid Funds, Inc.

800-LOAN USA (562-6872)

(page 50)

FAMILY CRISES

Al-Anon and Alateen

800-356-9996

[(212) 302-7240 in New York]

(page 56)

Alzheimer's Disease Foundation

800-621-0379

(Referrals to support groups and services)

Family Service America

800-221-2681

(page 58)

(Also see numbers under Abuse, Addiction and Alcoholism, Disabilities, and Health Care.)

HEALTH CARE

Juvenile **Diabetes** Foundation
800-223-1138
[(212) 889-7575 in New York]
(Information and referrals for treatment)

National **AIDS** Hotline
800-342-AIDS (342-2437)
(Public Health Service information)

National **Cancer** Institute
800-4-CANCER (422-6237)
(Information and referrals on treatment and support)

National Health Information Clearinghouse
800-336-4797
(page 66)

Shriner Hospital for Children
800-237-5055
[800-282-9161 in Florida]
(Information on free care for some children)

(Also see numbers under Addiction and Alcoholism, Disabilities, Family Crises, and Sexual Health.)

LEGAL MATTERS

National Criminal Justice Reference Service
800-638-8736
(page 73)

MENTAL HEALTH AND SUICIDE

Adolescent **Suicide** Hotline
800-621-4000
(page 78)

RUNNING AWAY

Child Find, Inc.
800-I-AM-LOST (426-5678)
(page 84)

Covenant House Nine-Line
800-999-9999
(page 84)

National Center for Missing and Exploited Children
800-843-5678
(Network of information and support)

National Runaway Switchboard
800-621-4000
(page 84)

Runaway Hotline
800-231-6946
[800-392-3352 in Texas]
(page 85)

SEXUAL HEALTH

National Clearinghouse for Health Information
800-336-4797

V.D. and Herpes Hotline
800-227-8922
(Advice, information, and referrals on sexually transmitted diseases from the American Social Health Association.)

(Also see numbers under Health Care.)

BACKUP

READING MATTER

The directories listed here can help you find the help you need. They are available at your school or public library. Since they are published yearly, or nearly so, try to use the most recent edition for up-to-date information.

Encyclopedia of Associations. Detroit: Gale Research Corp.
A three-volume listing of over 23,000 national and international organizations. Find the name of the group or the topic of your concern in the index.

National Directory of Addresses and Telephone Numbers. New York: Concord Reference Books.
An annual listing of 200,000 associations, businesses, research resources, and federal, state, and county governments.

National Directory of Children & Youth Services. Longmont, CO: Peterson Publishing.
A descriptive listing, with addresses and phone numbers, of public and private agencies, nationally and by state, that provide every sort of service for young people.

You can order these useful books by mail, by writing the organizations that publish them:

Directory of American Youth Organizations. A descriptive listing of service and volunteer groups for young people, from:
Father Flanagan's Boys' Home
Boys Town, NE 68010   Free

The Rights of Young People. A regularly updated guide to the laws affecting young people, from:
American Civil Liberties Union
132 West 43d Street
New York, NY 10036   About $5.00

Also distributed in bookstores or available from Bantam Books (800-223-6834).

The Self-Help Sourcebook. A listing of nearly 500 mutual support groups, networks, clearinghouses, and hotlines that provide help and information for a huge variety of problems, situations, diseases, and disorders, from:

New Jersey Self-Help Clearinghouse
St. Claires-Riverside Medical Center
Denville, NJ 07834 About $9.00

FALLBACKS

These organizations can offer suggestions if you need still more sources for help and information. They are involved in continual research about services for young people and maintain up-to-date files that should be useful.

Center for Early Adolescence
University of North Carolina at Chapel Hill
Suite 223, Carr Mill Mall
Carrboro, NC 27510
(919) 966-1148

The Children's Defense Fund
122 C Street, NW
Washington, DC 20001
(202) 628-8787

National Collaboration for Youth
1319 F Street, NW
Washington, DC 20004
(202) 347-2080

LIST OF ORGANIZATIONS

LIST OF ORGANIZATIONS

INDEX